Great Historical Coincidences

Great Historical Coincidences

How Good Luck Changed the Course of Science and History

PERE ROMANILLOS

KONECKY&KONECKY

Konecky & Konecky
72 Ayers Point Road
Old Saybrook, CT 06475

Original Title

Menuda Chiripa: Los Serendipias Más Famosas
© 2011, Pere Romanaillos
© 2011, Editorial Océano, S.L.

Translated by Janet Foster
English text copyright © Konecky & Konecky, 2016

ISBN: 978-1-56862-817-5

Printed in Korea

To Anna, who came into my life
by chance

Contents

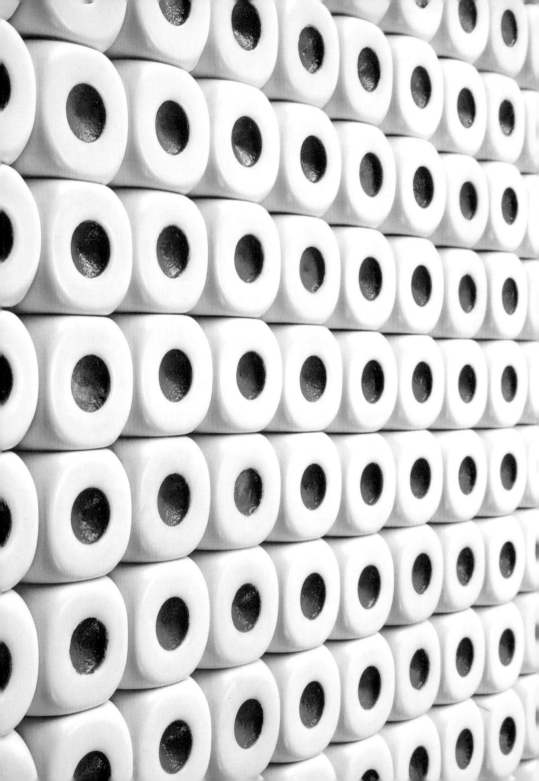

Life is Random

Chance favors the prepared mind.

Louis Pasteur (1822–1895)

I came to write this book purely by chance, having been drawn to this point by a few coincidences.

It all started when I was writing about the great mistakes of history, (published by K&K as *Great Historical Blunders*). This type of work requires a formidable amount of research. In the course of my investigations, I came across a document that expatiated upon the theme of serendipity and its role in the unfolding of important historical events, such as the discovery of America.

Great ideas usually occur to you when you are working… or thinking. The important thing is to be ready for them.

If I have learned anything during my years as a journalist and writer, it is to always be on the alert for themes that convey some knowledge, entertainment or fun to readers who make the effort to buy a book, newspaper or magazine. And serendipity was a subject that met these three characteristics.

To a great extent the job of an editor is to choose which idea among many is the best one. One of these could be serendipity.

Right away I discussed the idea with my editor, and once again luck was on my side. Publishers are very hard to please when it comes to accepting book proposals. The book has to be interesting, yet marketable at the same time (i.e., of interest to a large readership), but in this case, the theme of serendipity seduced my publisher from the get go. As luck would have it, the idea for this book occurred to me just a few days before they finalized their list.

For a great idea to come to fruition, you need to be able to manage it. The best thing to do is to quickly write down the event or discovery.

If you keep a sharp eye out, you may discover something that matters. It doesn't matter how many ideas you toss out. Keep searching.

If I had waited a few days more to present the topic, it's quite possible that now you would not be reading this introduction (or it would have been a year later before you had been able to do so).

The project was born under a lucky star, and the editorial board approved the idea. Being the passionate historians that we are, my editor and I enjoyed preparing a comprehensive list of contents. The idea was to address the theme of serendipity in a reasonably understandable (and especially fun) way through the great discoveries in history. Finally, we shortened our list of serendipities, leaving those whose development was the most curious and surprising — because the main objective of this book is to astonish the reader. We hope it does. Read on and see for yourself.

Seek and You Will...Find?

The essence of a word

The history of mankind is characterized by this yearning, the desire to encounter, to discover, to find what we seek. Some search for fame, others for fortune, some look for love, but most of us search for what we call happiness. Happiness can be finding our soul mate, landing our dream job, or finding something that we have been seeking for a long time. For some it takes a lifetime to finally attain it. But a lucky few find it without looking. Whatever the case, it is important to stay alert and read the signs that fate puts on our path that lead us to what we seek.

Serendipity is like a puzzle piece that we spend a long time trying to put in place, without success. Then we find the solution when we least expect it. Luck or determination?

The art of mixing work and experience with wisdom and good luck is a skill possessed by many of the

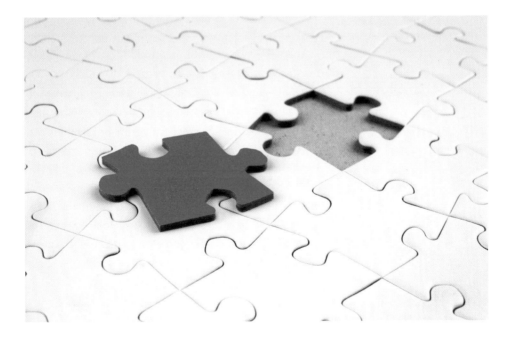

protagonists in this book. Whether physicists, chemists, astronomers, doctors, inventors or navigators, all consistently demonstrated a sharp sixth sense that helped them to find what they were seeking. Some found what they were looking for; many others ended up discovering something totally different, but just as good, or even better. Chance, luck, and good fortune manifested at the right time and place are all characteristics of serendipity, or the art of making unexpected discoveries purely by accident.

The history of "serendipity"

The term "serendipity" comes from an English neologism coined in 1754 by Horace Walpole, British politician and author. It first appears in one of many letters Walpole wrote to his friend, Sir Horatio (Horace) Mann:

Make no mistake. Serendipity has nothing in common with games of chance, although it could happen that when rummaging around in an old bookstore or record store, you find that rare copy that you weren't looking for, one that can make you filthy rich...

This discovery, indeed, is almost of that kind which I call *Serendipity,* a very expressive word, which, as I have nothing better to tell you, I shall endeavour to explain to you: you will understand it better by derivation than by the definition. I once read a silly fairy tale, called *The Three Princes of Serendip*: as their Highnesses travelled, they were always making discoveries, by accidents and sagacity, of things which they were not in quest of: for instance, one of them discovered that a mule blind in the right eye had traveled the same road lately, because the grass was only eaten on the left side, where it was worse than on the right — now do you understand *Serendipity*?

The three principles of serendipity

This eighteenth-century Persian tale about Serendip (Arabic name for the island of Ceylon, now Sri Lanka) is, in reality, an ancient legend that is also found, with some variations, in the Hebrew Talmud, in stories from ancient India, and in "The Story of the Sultan of Yemen and His Three Sons" from the *Arabian Nights*.

In this story it is told:

The King of Serendip had three sons. He instructed them to travel throughout the world solving problems, so that they would become educated and be able to govern his kingdom in the future.

During one of their journeys, the three princes were put to a test when they met a camel-driver who had lost his camel. Upon meeting them, he inquired about his animal:

"Have you seen my camel? I've lost it."

"Is it blind in one eye?" asked the eldest prince.

"Yes," said the camel-driver.

"Is it missing a tooth?" asked the middle prince.

"Yes, yes," replied the camel-driver.

"Is one foot lame?" inquired the youngest prince.

"It certainly is," acknowledged the camel-driver.

The three princes advised the camel-driver to walk to the place they had just come from, where he would surely find his lost camel. Thinking that they had seen it, the camel-driver was quick to follow their advice.

But he did not find his camel. So he then went back the way he came with the intention of returning to ask the princes again. At dusk he found them resting from their journey.

"Does your camel carry honey on one side and corn on the other?" asked the eldest prince.

"Yes, yes," said the man.

"Is a pregnant woman riding it?" asked the middle

Basil Rathbone as the detective Sherlock Holmes in the 1939 film *The Hound of the Baskervilles*. Holmes was the prototypical investigator: always alert and ready to make the most of luck in his discoveries.

prince.

"Yes, yes," replied the camel-driver.

"We do not know where it is, my good man," said the youngest prince.

But the camel-driver began to suspect that these foreign travelers had stolen the camel, the rider and its load because it was too much of a coincidence that they would know so many details. The camel-driver went to the city and brought the matter before the court, accusing them of being thieves.

The judge considered that there was cause to distrust them. They were arrested on suspicion of theft, and proceedings began that would either confirm their guilt, or absolve them.

Then it happened that the camel-driver found the animal roaming the countryside. Remorseful for having suspected the innocent travelers, he returned to the court and asked that the three nobles be released.

The judge, who up until this moment had not given them a chance to justify themselves, asked how they could know so much about the camel without having seen it.

"We saw its footprints on the road," said the eldest prince.

"One of the footprints was fainter than the other, so I figured that it was lame," said the middle prince.

"It had chewed the bushes on only one side of the road. Therefore it had to be blind in one eye," said the youngest noble.

If a camel is lost in the desert, it can be very difficult to find him again, since he can go many days without food or water.

"The leaves were ragged," said the eldest prince. "And this indicated that it had lost a tooth."

"Bees and ants on different sides of the road swarmed around something that had been deposited there. We saw that it was honey and corn," explained the middle prince.

"We also found some human hair that was so long, it made us think it was a woman's. And it was right where someone had stopped the animal and she had dismounted," declared the third prince.

"In the place where the person sat, we observed traces of the palms of both hands, which led us to conclude that she had to lean on them in order to sit down or stand up. Therefore we deduced that she was likely to be pregnant," said the eldest prince.

"Why did you not request clemency and to be heard by the judge in order to present these arguments in self-defense?" asked the lawyer.

Later on in the story of the three princes, their chance discoveries helped to save their lives.

"Because we felt that the camel-driver would keep looking and that it wouldn't be long before he found the beast," said the eldest prince.

"And that he would be generous enough to acknowledge his mistake and request our freedom," said the middle one.

"We also counted on it that the judge's natural curiosity would lead him to investigate," said the third prince.

"Arriving at the truth by their own methods would have been more beneficial to everyone than to insist on our innocence," said the first prince.

"Based on experience, we know that it is better when people arrive at the truth of their own accord," said the

second prince.

Astonished by their wisdom and cleverness, the judge released all three princes, who in the same manner continued on their long and fruitful path of learning.

Accidental discovery

The word "serendipity" fell into disuse until 1945 when the North American philosopher Walter Bradford Cannon, Emeritus Professor at Harvard, published a book entitled *The Way of an Investigator: A Scientist's Experience in Medical Research*. In his chapter on "Gains from Serendipity," he revived the word coined two centuries before by Walpole, showing several historical examples of scientific serendipity (some included in this book). In his text, Cannon defined serendipity as "the happy faculty, or luck, of finding unforeseen evidence of one's ideas or, with surprise, coming upon new objects or relations which were not being sought." The word was introduced gradually, and in 1955, the term appeared in the journal *Scientific American*, defined as a "chance observation falling on a receptive eye." Since 1974, most English dictionaries have defined serendipity as "the ability to make discoveries by accident and sagacity, when you are looking for something else."

Walter Bradford Cannon, professor at Harvard University (above: university entrance on Harvard Square) revived the word "serendipity" in his book *The Way of an Investigator: A Scientist's Experience in Medical Research*, published in 1945.

Its common use within the scientific community led to its adoption by the broader public. In fact, one of the best syntheses of the definition of serendipity, characterized by a mixture of chance and wisdom, comes from a scientist. It was Louis Pasteur who, in 1854, on the occasion of his inauguration as dean of the Faculty of Sciences at Lille (France), advised the young researchers: "By chance I can help, but remember that in the sciences of observation, chance only favors the prepared mind."

Recently, the word has served as the title of romantic comedy. Directed in 2001 by Peter Chelsom and starring John Cusack and Kate Beckinsale, the film adapts the meaning of the term to narrate the protagonists' encounter, thanks to a series of happy accidents and coincidences.

Types of Serendipity

Various authors, such as Pérez-Tamayo, Pek Van Andel and Royston M. Roberts, have classified serendipity in different categories, depending on how the discovery was made, also taking into account the way in which it came to be applied. Thus, we can distinguish the following types of serendipity.

Classic serendipity

This is a casual event that, thanks to the sagacity of the investigator, leads to the discovery of something that was not being sought. There are two types of classic serendipity.

Positive serendipity.

This occurs when a chance discovery has been applied correctly. The majority of serendipities included in this book are of this type. Thus the discovery of dynamite by Alfred Nobel in 1866, the discovery of X-rays by Röntgen in 1895, and of penicillin by Fleming in 1928, are all considered positive serendipities.

Negative serendipity.

This occurs when the finding is misinterpreted. The most

The term "serendipity" was coined in 1754 by Horace Walpole, Earl of Oxford, politician, writer, architect, and author of the famous novel *The Castle of Otranto*, which is considered the forerunner of the Gothic genre in literature.

notable case of negative serendipity is the discovery of America in 1492. Christopher Columbus was convinced that he had reached the East Indies, unaware that he had discovered a new continent full of unimaginable riches.

Pseudoserendipity

This term was coined in 1989 by the author Royston M. Roberts to characterize "accidental discoveries of ways to achieve an end sought for, in contrast to the meaning of (true) serendipity, which describes accidental discoveries of things not sought for." That is, those discoveries which come about because of a fortunate accident or a revelation after the scientist has been conducting research for a long time, but to no avail.

Clear examples of pseudoserendipity are the discovery of the Law of Universal Gravitation (Newton, 1666), the Archimedes' Principle, the vulcanization process (Goodyear, 1839) and the invention of photography (Daguerre, 1839). Pseudoserendipity abounds in specific disciplines such as chemistry, astronomy, biology, archeology and bacteriology. All of these pseudoserendipitous discoveries are characterized by an investigator's conscious and systematic search.

In general, we could say that serendipity is the result of luck or chance while pseudoserendipity is brought about through the effort of the researcher to whom the discovery comes as a revelation.

The discovery of America was a clear example of serendipity. The Spaniards were seeking a new route to India in order to facilitate their trade in spices: instead they found a new continent.

Elements of Serendipity

Most discoveries caused by an accidental or random event have a number of elements in common.

Curiosity and open perception.

How many times have you come across something fortuitously because it piqued your curiosity? Curiosity is an emotional state that accompanies uncertainty. It occurs when what we find is incomplete or not up to our expectations. This inspires us to open our perceptual awareness to our surroundings and to question all the data presented to us. This curiosity is, for example, what led the American scientist Baruch S. Blumberg to find the antigen responsible for Hepatitis B in 1963. His scientific curiosity led him to follow the trail of the antigen, analyzing blood samples at remote locations around the world, from America to Australia. In fact, it was the blood of an Australian aborigine that ultimately contained the elusive antigen.

Attention to facts.

Most serendipitous findings have been reached through careful observation of the facts investigated. Accidental or coincidental events serve no purpose if the researcher is not able to realize their significance and potential applications. Knowing how to "read" a coincidence is key to discovering what one is looking for. Therefore, it is important to be able to discard pre-established theories and know how to reorient research in a totally different direction.

Serendipity requires one to be looking for something, especially on a road full of obstacles.

This was the case, for example, in the accidental discovery of Viagra, the first effective oral treatment for erectile dysfunction. In 1996, pharmacologists at Pfizer Inc. were working with an active ingredient called sildenafil. The goal of the research was to fabricate a drug to combat high blood pressure and angina. But one of the noted side effects in the tested patients was that sildenafil induced erections. That gave them the lead to reorient the application of the drug and to end up producing the popular blue pill.

This ability of the researcher to focus on the facts and use them as a point of departure from previous theories was what enabled the English scientist and theologian Joseph Priestley to discover oxygen. This is how he recounted it in his book *Experiments and Observations on Different Kinds of Air:*

> To be honest, I must admit that at the beginning of the experiments, I was so far from having made any assumptions that would lead to the discoveries that have been achieved, that had anyone told me about them, I would have replied that it seemed very unlikely; and when the decisive facts were clearly prevailed to my attention, very slowly and with great hesitation, I yielded to the evidence of the senses.

Intuition and wisdom to understand the unknown. Often fortuitous events appearing in the course of an investigation are incomprehensible at first glance. And so it is through the researcher's wisdom and cunning that he is able to give appropriate relevance to what just occurred.

Normally, if one takes the time to follow a trail, the revelation will be almost instantaneous, as happened to Archimedes of Syracuse, who came up with his famous principle while bathing.

Scientific serendipities are extremely abundant, and the most frequent. Something that does not seem to be at all significant takes on new meaning when a scientist, perceiving a fortuitous or random fact arrives at what he was looking for, or finds something completely different. The important thing is the scientific dis-

Joseph Priestley (1733–1804) was a great scholar who made important discoveries, including several gases such as oxygen, which he had not expected to find, and around which he developed an unlikely theory that later proved false.

covery itself, beyond the phenomenon observed or whether or not it was arrived at in a premeditated manner. As Albert Einstein said:

> Science, as something existing and complete, is the most objective thing known to man. But science in the making, science as an end to be pursued, is as subjective and psychologically conditioned as any other branch of human endeavor.

Traits such as creativity, imagination, curiosity and inspiration have played an important role in the history of great discoveries.

Archimedes was one of the greatest mathematicians of antiquity. Many of his discoveries were later recorded in the tenth-century Palimpsest, which included some of his work. But this too was to disappear when it was later overwritten by a liturgical text. Finally, by the grace of serendipity, an academic rediscovered the work in Istanbul in the nineteenth century.

PHYSICS AND ASTRONOMY

Eureka!

WHAT? Archimedes' Principle

When?
Third century B.C.E. during the Punic Wars between Rome and Carthage.

Who?
Archimedes of Syracuse mathematician, physicist, engineer, astronomer and inventor.

How and Where?
In Syracuse, during a leisurely bath, he observed how his body displaced the water, while pondering whether the crown of Hiero II was pure gold or if silver had been added.

Archimedes' Principle:

A body immersed wholly or partially in a static fluid experiences an upward buoyancy equal to the weight of the fluid displaced by the volume of said body.

While Archimedes was turning over the problem in his mind, he happened to arrive at the baths. There, seated in the tub, he noticed that the amount of water that splashed over the edge was equal to the amount by which his body was immersed. He had discovered how to solve the problem. Overcome with joy, he jumped out of the tub and ran naked to his house, shouting loudly that he had found what he had been looking for.

De Architectura, Marcus Vitruvius Pollio

This famous scene of Archimedes has been passed down to us thanks to the description made by Vitruvius in his book *De Architectura*. According to this account by the famous Roman architect, it all began at the insistence of Hiero II, the ruler of Syracuse between 270 and 215 B.C.E. It seems that the Greek tyrant was suspicious about the authenticity of a crown supposedly made of pure gold. He was convinced that the royal goldsmith had added silver to the piece. And so he asked his wise man (Archimedes of Syracuse) to attempt to resolve the question without damaging the crown.

Hiero was a cruel and ruthless monarch. Archimedes got to work immediately so as not to disappoint him. The simplest thing to do would have been to melt down the crown and turn it into a regular mass in order to calculate its density. But this was not allowed. He was

If Hiero's crown had silver incorporated into it but weighed the same as pure gold, its volume would have been greater because silver is less dense than gold.

entirely preoccupied by this problem when the famous serendipity occurred.

He was bathing in a bathhouse when he noticed how the water level rose when he submerged himself in the tub. In this unremarkable setting, he immediately realized that he had stumbled upon the way to calculate the density of the royal crown. The story recounts that the Greek sage ran home naked to try out what he had discovered. Once there, Archimedes began to calculate the volume of water displaced by one piece of gold, one of silver, and by the crown of the monarch. After submerging the three pieces in a bowl of water, he determined their relative densities, compared them and discovered the deception. The density of the crown was between 10.5 and 19.3 grams per cubic centimeter, which corresponded to the combined densities of silver and gold.

Upon learning of the deceit, the king commanded that the unfortunate officer be executed immediately.

Thus was born the principle of hydrostatics, famously known as Archimedes' principle, which states: "A body immersed wholly or partially in a static fluid experiences an upward buoyant force equal to the weight of the fluid displaced by the volume of said body."

In order to improve hygiene, public baths were one of the greatest Roman inventions. It had to have been, however, a small tub where Archimedes observed the displacement of water produced by his body when submerged.

What Does "Eureka" Mean?

The story goes that upon discovering the principle of hydrostatics, Archimedes ran out naked into the street shouting, "Eureka!" The word has been associated with great inventions and discoveries ever since. Eureka is the first person singular perfect tense of the Greek verb *eurisko*, which means "find." So, what Archimedes was really shouting through the streets of Syracuse was, "I found it! I found it!"

The Most Famous Apple in History

WHAT? The Universal Law of Gravitation

When?
1666: the year of the Great Fire of London.

Who?
Isaac Newton (1643–1727), physicist, alchemist, mathematician and inventor.

How?
While contemplating the fortuitous drop of an apple in his garden. This anecdote appears in *Memoirs of Sir Isaac Newton's Life*, published in 1752 by his friend William Stukeley.

What we know is a drop, what we don't know is an ocean.
Isaac Newton

Before we begin, let us clarify one issue. However co-incidental or haphazard a discovery may seem, whether in the field of medicine, physics or archeology, usually a considerable amount of work and intellectual effort has gone into it. So proclaims one of the inspirational phrases in this book: "Chance favors the prepared mind."

Sir Isaac Newton, one of the most brilliant thinkers who ever lived, certainly fits that description. Historically known for his laws of kinematics, the corpuscular theory of light and the development of differential and integral calculus, his most famous achievement was the Law of Universal Gravitation. Many regard this discovery as the culmination of the scientific revolution. His famous formula ($F = G \times m_1 \times m_2 / r_2$) gave birth to a systematic understanding of the nature of the physical phenomena of the universe, that was anticipated by the discoveries of Copernicus, Kepler and Galileo.

But what does this famous law actually mean? So that we understand it: the formula states that every object in the universe that possesses mass exerts a gravitational pull on other objects with mass. As Newton demonstrated, the more mass an object has, the greater is its force of attraction. Similarly, the gravitational force decreases as these bodies are separated (that is what happens to astronauts when they leave Earth's gravitational field and float around inside their spaceships). For example, this force is what causes Earth to revolve around the Sun at a distance of more than 93 million miles, and the Moon to do the same around Earth. And the Moon's magnetic pull causes the tides of our seas and oceans.

Statue of Newton at Trinity College Cambridge.

Closer to home, gravity is what enables us to jump and not shoot upwards, because its force anchors us to the ground. The very evolution of man has a close relationship with the force of gravity. More than two hundred bones of the human skeleton are designed to interact with the force of gravity, as are our muscles. Without gravity, there would be no need to rise up or to bear weight, and our muscles would be atrophied from disuse. Hence, astronauts need physical recuperation after a long period in a non-gravitational environment.

But let us return to Newton. Two coincidences marked the development of his famous universal law. In the year 1666 Trinity College, Cambridge University (where Newton was an undergraduate student with few resources, paying his keep by doing small jobs in the community) had to shut down suddenly because a plague was ravaging the area. The young Englishman (23 years old at the time) returned to Woolsthorpe Manor, near Grantham in Lincolnshire, to the modest house where he was born. It was there that in a short period of two years, he would achieve breakthroughs in diverse fields including mathematics, optics, physics and astronomy.

But what really elevated him to the annals of great scientific discoverers happened in the garden of the house. Obsessed by the orbital forces of the Moon around Earth, Newton contemplated the issue day in, day out.

Then one afternoon in 1666, he went for a stroll

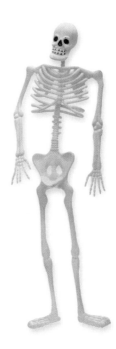

The design of the human skeleton has evolved to respond to the earth's gravitational forces.

· ·

One afternoon in 1666, Newton was strolling in his garden when by chance an apple fell on his head and changed the course of science.

· ·

Why does an apple always fall downwards? Because Earth exerts a pull equivalent to its mass, which is the sum of the gravitational force of each of its atoms.

Newton, portrayed by William Blake as the divine geometrician who gives structure to the universe.

through the garden of his house. This was when the second coincidence occurred: the fall of an apple inspired his famous Law of Universal Gravitation. It seems impossible that such an advanced theory was prompted by such a commonplace occurrence. Skeptics can refer to a manuscript in the collection of the Royal Society that tells how it happened, in the handwriting of William Stukeley, Newton's friend and author of a biography of the scientist:

After dinner, the weather being warm, we went into the garden, & drank tea under the shade of some apple trees, only he [Newton], & myself. Amidst other discourse, he told me he was just in the same situation, as when formerly the notion of gravitation came into his mind. Why should that apple always descend perpendicularly to the ground, thought he to himself, occasion'd by the fall of an apple, as he sat in a contemplative mood. Why should it not go sideways, or upwards? But constantly to the earths centre? Assuredly, the reason is that the earth draws it. There must be a drawing power in matter. And the sum of the drawing power in the matter of the earth must be in the earth's center, not in any side of the earth. Therefore does this apple fall perpendicularly, or toward the center? if matter thus draws matter, it must be in proportion of its quantity. Therefore the apple draws the earth, as well as the earth draws the apple.

This astonishing manuscript can be accessed on the website of the Royal Society: http://royalsociety.org/turning-the-pages.

Unfortunately, those who would like to visit the famous apple tree will be disappointed. The original no

Did you know?

The remains of this brilliant scientist rest in the famous Westminster Abbey, along with other major British figures such as Charles Darwin, Charles Dickens and Alexander Pope. His epitaph reads:

> Here lies SIR ISAAC NEWTON, this knight with mental acumen bordering on the divine and mathematical principles uniquely his, was the first to show the form and movements of the planets, the paths of comets and the ebb and flow of the ocean. He carefully investigated the varying refrangibility of rays of light and the color properties caused by them. An interpreter who was diligent and wise, he was faithful to the laws of nature, antiquity, and the Holy Scriptures. In his philosophy he defended the majesty of the Almighty and in his behavior expressed the humility of the Gospel. We mortals give thanks that there has existed among us so great an ornament of the human race!

longer exists. But if you visit Newton's birthplace (see visiting hours at http://www.nationaltrust.org.uk/woolsthorpe-manor), you can see an example, descended from a cutting of the famous apple tree.

In the archives of the British Royal Society, there exists a piece of wood that belonged to the original tree. In May of 2010, to celebrate the 350th anniversary of this scientific society, the astronaut Piers Sellers brought it with him into space on NASA's mission number STS 132.

The Earth Moves

WHAT? The Aberration of Light

When?
1666, the year of the founding of the French Academy of Sciences.

Who?
James Bradley (1693–1762), Astronomer Royal to the English Crown.

How?
Observing a wind vane while navigating the River Thames.

We begin by explaining what is meant by the aberration of light. It is none other than the difference between the observed and actual position of a star that results from the velocity of the observer and the finite speed of light. Here is a good analogy to help us understand it better: Let's imagine that it's raining, and we open an umbrella and stand in place. The raindrops fall vertically onto the umbrella, and we don't get wet. But if we begin to move forward rapidly, the rain seems to fall increasingly at an incline, which forces us to tilt the umbrella to avoid getting wet. This is an analogy of what happens when we observe the stars. The rotation of Earth, its orbital movement around the Sun, and the movement of the entire solar system itself, produces an apparent displacement of the rays of light produced by whatever celestial object we are observing from Earth through a telescope, and therefore, a misperception of its true position.

Here is another example related to rain. Let's imagine that we are riding in a car, and it starts to rain. As we move under a vertical downpour, we have the impression that it is hitting the windshield at an incline. Similarly, the light of a star observed from the ground appears slightly deflected and displaced as a consequence. The maximum shift is termed the "constant of aberration," which has an accepted value of 20.49552 arcseconds.

Now let's talk about its discoverer, James Bradley who served as Astronomer Royal to the English Crown after Edmund Halley, discoverer of the famous comet of the same name. Born in a small village in Gloucester (United Kingdom), he studied at Oxford and was ordained a vicar at the age of 26. Passionate about astronomy, he reconciled his ecclesiastical duties with his astronomical observations and studies, and went

James Bradley (1693–1762) by Thomas Hudson. He succeeded Edmund Halley as Astronomer Royal to the English court, and enjoyed a high reputation.

If the direction of the wind direction can be seen differently depending on a boat's course, the light of a star must also be different depending on the motion of Earth.

Observation of the sky during a long photographic exposure. The stars appear to rotate in the sky, when in fact it is we on Earth who turn.

on to become a professor of astronomy at the University of Oxford.

Bradley was particularly attracted to the study of stellar parallax. The term is based on the apparent shift in position of a star caused by the movement of Earth from one end to another of its orbit. He was working with his colleague Samuel Molyneux (a wealthy amateur astronomer) when, by chance, they found an explanation for this inexplicable change of stellar location.

It happened during a cruise on the Thames. Suddenly the boat Bradley was navigating changed course, and the wind vane on the mast also changed position. "How unusual!" he thought. "The position of the wind vane has changed, but the direction of the wind remains the same. Why is that?" Clearly, the change had occurred in the direction of the boat relative to the wind direction. It dawned on Bradley that the movement of the stars was produced in a similar way. They were not moving. The change was actually caused by the motion of Earth itself. If the wind direction could change in relation to the ship's course, the light of a star could also undergo changes according to the movement of Earth, now that it was being observed from a different location in space.

Bradley named his discovery the "aberration of light," and proved definitively that the apparent movement of the stars was actually the movement of Earth. He published his findings in the *Philosophical Transactions* of the Royal Society in 1729.

186,000 Miles per Second

WHAT? The Speed of Light

When?
1675, the year the Royal Observatory in Greenwich is founded.

Who?
Ole Römer (1644–1710), Danish astronomer hired by Jean-Baptiste Colbert to work in the French court of Louis XIV.

How?
Observing the eclipses of Jupiter's moons. Io's shadow would not have appeared had the corresponding speed of light been infinite.

They say that good things, if brief, are twice as good. This maxim applied perfectly to the scientist Ole Römer in the seventeenth century. Under an illuminating title, "Demonstration that Light Moves," the Danish astronomer needed little more than one sheet (published on December 7, 1676, by the *Journal des Savants*, the oldest literary and scientific journal in Europe) to earn a place of honor in the history of great scientific discoveries.

Until his brilliant analysis, the scientific community was convinced that the speed of light was infinite. To the human eye it seemed that light was instantaneous and that there was nothing to measure. This was the belief of renowned scientists such as the Italian Galileo Galilei, who in his experiments to determine the speed of light covered and uncovered two separate lanterns positioned at a distance of 1.5 kilometers apart. There seemed to be no time at all between when he uncovered his lantern and when he saw his collaborator's response. And so he wrote: "If the appearance of the opposite light is not instantaneous, at least it is extremely rapid, almost immediate."

The Danish astronomer Ole Römer (1644–1710) discovered that the speed of light was not infinite while studying the eclipses of Io, a satellite of Jupiter. The planet's shadow was visible before Earth was closest to Jupiter.

A century later, everything was to change as a result of Römer's investigations. He began by making observations of Jupiter and the orbits of its satellites. It was then that the Danish astronomer realized that the eclipse that caused the planet's shadow to appear on one of its moons (Io) was visible from Earth earlier than anticipated when our planet was approaching Jupiter in its orbit around the Sun. Likewise, the eclipse was later when Earth moved away from Jupiter. Something that might seem obvious today caused a real stir at the time. Thus, Römer concluded that these delays or advances must be due to the speed of light, and coincidentally discovered its finite speed (his estimate was 225,000 km per second).

Over the centuries, many have tried to accurately measure the exact speed of light in space. It is currently fixed

Light travels at different speeds depending on the medium through which it travels. It goes at a slightly slower speed through air than space.

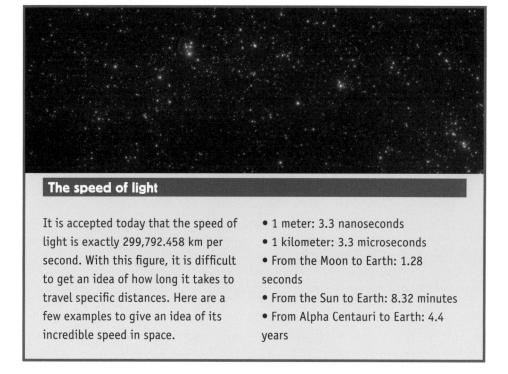

The speed of light

It is accepted today that the speed of light is exactly 299,792.458 km per second. With this figure, it is difficult to get an idea of how long it takes to travel specific distances. Here are a few examples to give an idea of its incredible speed in space.

- 1 meter: 3.3 nanoseconds
- 1 kilometer: 3.3 microseconds
- From the Moon to Earth: 1.28 seconds
- From the Sun to Earth: 8.32 minutes
- From Alpha Centauri to Earth: 4.4 years

at around 1.08 billion kilometers per hour. This was a speed that everyone could see live during the conversation between NASA's Christopher C. Kraft, Jr. at Mission Control Center in Houston and the astronaut Neil Armstrong. After each question asked from the base, the response of our first man on the Moon took more than two seconds to reach Earth.

An Accidental Experiment

WHAT? The Theory of Electromagnetism

When?
1820, the year George III of England dies after 59 years on the throne and is succeeded by his son George IV.

Who?
Hans Christian Oersted (1777–1851) while passing an electric current near a compass.

How?
During a simple experiment with his students in a college class, Oersted observed that the needle deviated noticeably toward the current.

In the early nineteenth century, the scientific community was still not very clear on the relationship between electricity and magnetism, considering the latter as a phenomenon exclusive to steel and iron. However, there had been indications that something happens between the two forces. Sailors had often told of sudden changes in magnetic orientation systems during lightning storms at sea, but scientists did not fully grasp the connection.

It was Hans Christian Oersted, a professor of Electricity, Galvanism and Magnetism at the University of Copenhagen (Denmark), who finally discovered the relationship, purely by chance. While teaching a class to his students about the conversion of electricity into heat, as chance would have it, he placed a compass near a current of electricity being generated by a battery (invented 20 years previously by Count Alessandro Volta). At that moment, he was able to observe that the magnetic compass needle was oriented toward the electrical source. Amazed, he repeated the operation by varying the position of the compass. Wherever he placed it, the needle always ended up pointing towards the source of electricity. He had just discovered electromagnetism. Oersted did not stop there; in subsequent experiments, he interposed different elements between the conductor and the compass. To his surprise, he found that in all cases the electromagnetic force went through any type of material. Oersted published the results of his research in a single article entitled "Experimenta circa effectum conflictus electrici in acum magneticam."

Before long other scientists began working along the same lines. André-Marie Ampere, Michael Faraday and others expanded on Oersted's discoveries, making de-

Statue of Hans Christian Oersted in Oerstedsparken in Copenhagen, Denmark. Holder of a degree in medicine, his great passion was chemistry, particularly electromagnetic forces.

• •

The Electromagnetic Theory proved that both electric and magnetic fields were manifestations of a single field. Furthermore, the nature of light was explained as an electromagnetic wave.

• •

tailed descriptions of the magnetic forces induced by electric currents. Faraday ended up proving something very new at the time: he discovered that it was possible to generate an electric field by means of a magnetic field. This phenomenon is nowadays the basis for many technological applications, such as engines and battery-powered electric generators, as well as transformers and induction furnaces. His work culminated in Maxwell's equations and the demonstration of electromagnetic waves by Heinrich Hertz (1888).

In honor of the Danish scientist's discovery, the unit that measures the intensity of the magnetic field is named "Oersted."

The electromagnetic crane, one of the applications of electromagnetism, is composed of a magnetic material such as iron, with an electric wire attached. The result is a powerful magnet that can lift materials of great weight and size, as in the case of demolitions.

An overlooked discovery

In addition to being considered the father of electromagnetism, Oersted has also gone down in history for being the first to isolate aluminum, by electrolysis, in 1825. This recognition came a bit late because this discovery was overlooked in older works on the history of chemistry. The honor due to him was finally bestowed in 1920 (almost 100 years after the event) when, on the centenary of the discovery, a Danish chemist repeated the procedure described by Oersted and managed to extract pure aluminum. Better late than never...

Magic Rays

WHAT? X-Rays: Invisible Electromagnetic Radiation

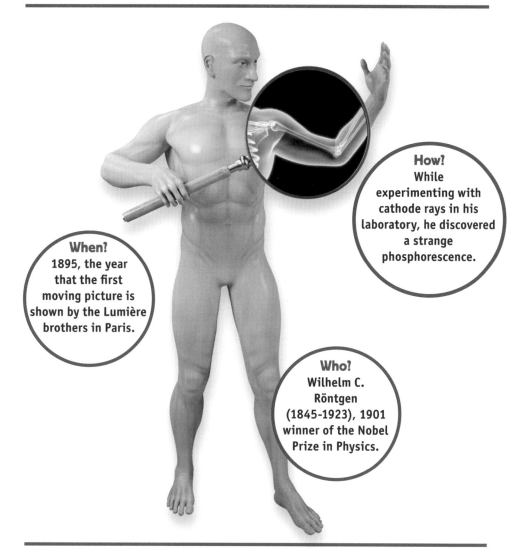

How?
While experimenting with cathode rays in his laboratory, he discovered a strange phosphorescence.

When?
1895, the year that the first moving picture is shown by the Lumière brothers in Paris.

Who?
Wilhelm C. Röntgen (1845-1923), 1901 winner of the Nobel Prize in Physics.

It all began in 1878. William Crookes, a renowned English chemist, focused his research on the conduction of electricity in gases, work that resulted in an invention called the "Crookes tube." It consists of an empty glass container inside of which a variety of gases are circulating. When electricity is applied, the gases acquire fluorescence by the action of cathode rays, or currents of electrons. This cathode ray tube was the seed of what in the future would become the first television systems.

Several researchers began to work with him, although in 1887 a New York engineer, Nikola Tesla, found that exposure to such radiation could be hazardous to biological organisms.

This warning did not deter that other research scientist, Wilhelm Conrad Röntgen. The Prussian physicist analyzed the cathode rays but wanted to avoid the violet fluorescence produced on the walls of the tube. On the night of November 8, 1895, Röntgen was in his darkened laboratory performing the previously mentioned experiment. He covered his Crookes tube with black cardboard. Charging the coil one last time, he noticed a faint greenish-yellow glow in the back of the lab. He set up a small screen coated with a solution of crystals of barium platinum-cyanide. He turned off the fluorescent tube and, to his surprise, the brightness on the screen remained undiminished. He positioned the coated sample farther away and found that the fluorescence was still being produced.

Röntgen determined that these rays were capable of generating radiation that was deeply penetrating and completely invisible.

During the following weeks, Röntgen thoroughly studied these mysterious rays. He even began to photograph these sessions, and it was at this point that a second coincidence occurred. All of the photographic plates that he kept concealed in a drawer in the laboratory had been

The English chemist William Crookes (1832–1919) was the discoverer of thallium and the inventor of the Crookes tube, which served as a starting point for the X-Rays that Röntgen discovered while working with him. Crookes was an important researcher who promoted science over spiritualism, attempting to provide scientific explanations for paranormal phenomena. Among other things, he discovered a system to separate gold from silver.

• •

Upon seeing history's first radiographic image of the human body, Anna Röntgen could not help but exclaim: "I have seen my own death!"

• •

exposed. Surely this had to do with the mysterious rays. In order to verify this, he placed a wooden box containing a pair of weights on top of a photographic plate. He connected the tube. The rays penetrated the wood, and to his surprise the image of the weights was impressed on the plate. Encouraged by the unexpected result, Röntgen continued testing with disparate objects, such as a compass and the barrel of a shotgun.

Finally, on December 22, 1895, Röntgen decided to try his experiment on a human being. His wife, Anna Bertha, volunteered and placed her hand on a photographic plate, exposing it to the invisible rays for 15 minutes. When the plate was developed, there appeared an image of historic importance in the future development of medicine: the exposed bones of her hand and her wedding ring as well. Upon seeing history's first radiographic image of the human body, Anna could not help but exclaim: "I have seen my own death!"

A new branch of medicine had just been born: radiology. Six days later, on December 28, 1895, Röntgen published the article "On a New Kind of Rays." The German physicist explained the properties of the unknown rays or X:

> The justification of the term "rays," applied to the phenomena, lies partly in the regular shadow pictures produced by the interposition of a more or less permeable body between the source and a photographic plate or fluorescent screen.

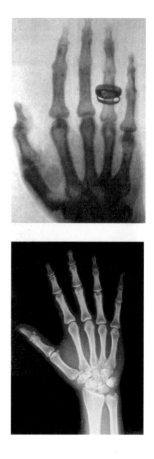

Above, image made on December 22, 1895 by William Röntgen. Below, a modern radiograph.

I have observed and photographed many such shadow pictures. . . . I also have a shadow of the bones of the hand; of a wire wound upon a bobbin; of a set of weights in a box of a compass card and a needle completely enclosed in a metal case; of a piece of metal where the X-rays show the want of homogeneity, and of other things.

The discovery caused a real stir in the scientific community. Röntgen received several awards. Kaiser Wilhelm II of Germany granted him the Order of the Crown; he was also honored with the Rumford Medal by the Royal Society of London in 1896, with the Barnard Medal by Columbia University, and in 1901 he received the Nobel Prize in Physics. The president of the Royal Swedish Academy of Sciences made the following remarks during the ceremony on December 10, 1901:

The Academy awarded the Nobel Prize in Physics to Wilhelm Conrad Röntgen, Professor in the University of Munich, for the discovery with which his name is linked for all time: the discovery of the so-called Röntgen rays or, as he himself called them, X-rays. These are, as we know, a new form of energy and have received the name "rays" on account of their property of propagating themselves in straight lines as light does.

The actual constitution of this radiation of energy is still unknown. Several of its characteristic properties have, however, been discovered first by Röntgen himself and then by other physicists who have directed their researches into this field. And there is no doubt that much success will be gained in physical science when this strange energy form is sufficiently investigated and its wide field thoroughly explored.

Let us remind ourselves of but one of the properties which have been found in Röntgen rays; that which is

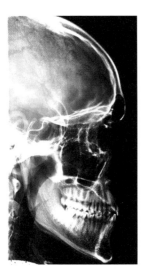

An exposure of several minutes is needed to make a picture with X-rays, which would be very dangerous to living subjects. Radiographs, on the other hand, contain contaminants, and should be brought to pharmacies for recycling.

the basis of the extensive use of X-rays in medical practice. Many bodies, just as they allow light to pass through them in varying degrees, behave likewise with X-rays, but with the difference that some which are totally impenetrable to light can easily be penetrated by X-rays, while other bodies stop them completely.

Thus, for example, metals are impenetrable to them; wood, leather, cardboard and other materials are penetrable and this is also the case with the muscular tissues of animal organisms. Now, when a foreign body impenetrable to X-rays, e.g. a bullet or a needle, has entered these tissues its location can be determined by illuminating the appropriate part of the body with X-rays and taking a shadowgraph of it on a photographic plate, whereupon the impenetrable body is immediately detected.

The importance of this for practical surgery, and how many operations have been made possible and facilitated by it is well known to all. If we add that in many cases severe skin diseases, e.g. lupus, have been successfully treated with Röntgen rays, we can say at once that Röntgen's discovery has already brought so much benefit to mankind that to reward it with the Nobel Prize fulfills the intention of the testator to a very high degree.

Röntgen never applied for a patent for his discovery; he donated X-Rays to humanity. In 1928, the röntgen (R), a unit of measurement of ionization produced by radiation, was created in his honor.

Wilhelm Röntgen, son of a weaver, was born in Prussia. His family emigrated to the Netherlands when he was three years old. Eventually, he settled in Germany, where his work at the University of Munich earned him the Nobel Prize in Physics in 1901.

Radioactivity Out of a Drawer

WHAT? Radioactivity

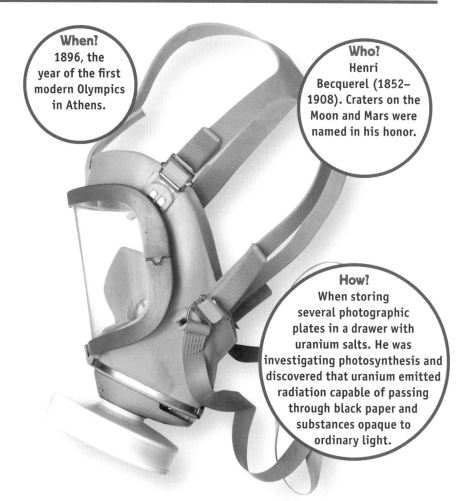

When?
1896, the year of the first modern Olympics in Athens.

Who?
Henri Becquerel (1852–1908). Craters on the Moon and Mars were named in his honor.

How?
When storing several photographic plates in a drawer with uranium salts. He was investigating photosynthesis and discovered that uranium emitted radiation capable of passing through black paper and substances opaque to ordinary light.

Sometimes it is better to stop what you're doing and wait for chance to take its course. This was the case with the French physicist Henri Becquerel, considered the discoverer of radioactivity, even though it was by an absurd coincidence.

He was educated and nurtured in a family of scientists. His grandfather Antoine César Becquerel was one of the founders of electrochemistry, and his father Alexandre-Edmond Becquerel discovered the photovoltaic effect. In 1894, Becquerel was appointed chief engineer of the French Ministry of Roads and Bridges. But he preferred scientific experimentation. So he took his first steps by investigating the rotation of polarized light and stimulating phosphorescent crystals with infrared light.

At the age of 43, this restless Parisian scientist turned his attention to the work of Wilhelm Röntgen, who had just discovered electromagnetic radiation at wavelengths corresponding to X-Rays. Without thinking twice, Becquerel threw himself into emulating the Prussian scientist's experiments. To do this, he wrapped a photographic plate in dark paper, placed it on a chunk of uranium, and exposed it to sunlight for four hours. After a period of time, Becquerel took the bundle to the darkroom and revealed the photographic plate. As if by magic, the image of the chunk of uranium appeared, confirming that the mineral did indeed emit X-Rays.

The Frenchman Henri Becquerel was born in Paris and raised in a scientific environment. His grandfather was one of the pioneers of the study of the electromagnetic phenomena, and his father studied light and phosphorescence. Like them, he served as professor of the French National Museum of Natural History in Paris.

But a good scientist is suspicious by nature, so he decided to repeat the experiment. He prepared several photographic plates, and placed a chunk of uranium on each one. The problem was that this was Paris, and the sun was often absent. The cloudy days followed one after the next, and Becquerel got tired of waiting. He grabbed all of his equipment and put it in a desk drawer to wait for a sunny day. But since the bad weather did not stop, the scientist decided to give up on his

In the International System of Units, a unit of radioactivity was named the "becquerel" (Bq) in his honor.

experiment and empty the drawer. To his considerable astonishment, he saw that the silhouettes of the chunks of uranium were clearly evident on all of the photographic plates. This had occurred in complete darkness, without sunlight or phosphorescence. Thus, Becquerel discovered the uncanny ability of uranium to emit constant radiation without light or electricity.

This natural physical phenomenon would in the future be harnessed to create energy, and used in medicine (radio-therapy and radiology) and for industrial applications (such as measuring thickness and density). In the International System of Units, a unit of radioactivity was named the "becquerel" (Bq) in his honor.

But Pierre and Marie Curie were truly the ones who developed the theory of radioactivity. Both the Curies and Henri Becquerel were awarded the Nobel Prize for Physics in 1903, "In recognition of the extraordinary services they have rendered by their joint researches on the radiation phenomena." Marie Curie continued to investigate and in 1910 was able to demonstrate how to extract one gram of pure radium. She was awarded a second Nobel Prize (this time in Chemistry), "In recognition of her services to the advancement of chemistry by the discovery of the elements radium and polonium, by the isolation of radium and the study of the nature and compounds of this remarkable element." She never patented the radium isolation process, instead donating it to the scientific community.

Commemorative stamp in honor of Marie Curie. She and her husband Pierre were the scientists who actually developed the Theory of Radioactivity.

The history of a disquieting symbol

Most of us recognize the symbol that warns of the presence of radioactivity. The well- known black circle with three black blades on a yellow background, an indicator of danger in the natural world, came into being in 1946. A group of engineers in California were debating what might be the best way to signal the danger posed by radioactive materials. Of the various designs proposed, they finally decided on a circle representing an atom, and three lines symbolizing the contaminating rays.

At first the drawing was magenta on a blue background. But back then, magenta pigment was costly to produce, and the blue background rendered it almost invisible outdoors. So they changed their minds and put it on a yellow background. But then many complained that the color was quite present in the laboratory and that the symbol would go unnoticed. It was impossible to reach an agreement. Finally, an independent agency intervened to regulate the process. The designers Bill Ray and George Warlick were commissioned to execute the work. After several sketches, the famous black symbol on a yellow background was finally approved. It remained in use until 1994, when the International Atomic Energy Agency (IAEA) presented a new symbol, a triangle on a red background composed of three drawings: three blades emitting radiation, a skull and a person running away.

Radiation hazard symbol. The combination of black and yellow is a warning sign in nature. It can be found on many poisonous animals, such as wasps.

An Engineer with a Sweet Tooth

WHAT? The Microwave Oven

When?
1946, the year UNICEF and the NBA are founded and Italy is declared a republic.

Who?
Percy Spencer (1894–1970), engineer with the Raytheon Corporation.

How?
When he found that a chocolate bar that had been in his pocket while he was experimenting with a magnetron had melted completely. Then he tried grains of corn, and they instantly popped, filling the entire room with popcorn.

It's surprising that such an everyday appliance like the microwave oven has its origins in the military. Shortly before the outbreak of the Second World War, the world looked with concern at German rearmament, and other countries began preparing for the impending conflict. Nazi propaganda claimed that the Germans had developed the so-called death ray, able to destroy entire cities through radio waves. The government of the United Kingdom was alarmed, and commissioned H. E. Wimperis, chief scientific adviser to the British Royal Air Force, to determine whether or not Germany was bluffing. Wimperis contacted the Scottish physicist Robert Watson-Watt to find out if the Nazi's invention was feasible. Watson-Watt said that it was impossible but noted that his team would work on the "still difficult, but less unpromising problem of radio-detection as opposed to radio-destruction" in order to locate targets. In short, radar.

On February 12, 1935, Watson-Watt sent a memorandum on the proposed system entitled "Detection and Location of Aircraft by Radio Methods." Although it was not the famous death ray, it had clear applications. The upper echelons of the British army immediately requested a demonstration of this invention. A secret meeting was convened, attended by Watson-Watt, his assistant Arnold Wilkins and one member of the Air Ministry (A.P. Rowe). The radar system devised by Watson-Watt was repeatedly able to locate an airplane, and the British government began developing several stations that would end up being decisive in the future conflict.

One of the key elements of radar is a device called a magnetron. This is what transforms electrical energy into electromagnetic energy in the form of microwaves, thereby fueling the radar by means of a powerful radio-

Popcorn reveals in an instant the utility of the microwave oven, which moves water molecules and orients them in one direction at high speed, causing the temperature to rise quickly.

In fact, Percy Spencer was himself irradiated with electromagnetic waves from the magnetron, as the chocolate bar melted in his pocket.

electric source. When 1946 rolled around, the American engineer Dr. Percy Spencer was working with the previously mentioned magnetron in his laboratory at the Raytheon Company. At the end of several consecutive tests, he got hungry and remembered that he had a chocolate bar in his pocket. He was out of luck. He reached for it only to discover that it had melted completely. This piqued his scientific curiosity. He put two and two together and hypothesized that waves from the magnetron had something to do with the incident. So he conducted an experiment. This time he put a few grains of corn near the traveling-wave tube transmitter, connected the magnetron...and voila! The corn started popping.

Modern microwave oven. Some cookbooks offer genuine haute cuisine recipes using them.

Next up Spencer tried a chicken egg. It started to vibrate and finally exploded due to the effect of the waves. This was promising, as it seemed that the cause could be attributed to exposure to the low density energy of the microwaves of the magnetron.

The next step in the research was to design a metal box with an opening through which the energy of the microwaves could enter. Thus, he sought to generate an electromagnetic field of higher density. He continued trying different foods and in all cases found that the temperature increased rapidly. He had invented the microwave oven.

That same year, the Raytheon Company applied for a patent, and in 1947, the first commercial microwave oven appeared on the market. The appliance was a bit cumbersome. It was five feet tall, weighed 175 pounds and was very expensive: $5,000. Naturally, sales were somewhat disappointing. Technological advances enabled the microwave to evolve to a more practical size, and a more competitive price. But then rumors began about the health risk of microwaves to consumers. That delayed its popular acceptance somewhat, but by the early seventies, sales of microwave ovens exceeded the number of gas stoves for the first time. In 1978, more than 9 million American kitchens contained this practical appliance. Its popularity continued to rise and even began to change cooking habits: "fast food" had come into its own.

Percy Spencer continued to be a consultant at the Raytheon Company until his death at the age of 76.

The first microwave weighed about 175 lbs. Fortunately, they are considerably smaller today.

Holographic Images

WHAT? Holography or the Recreation of a Wavefront

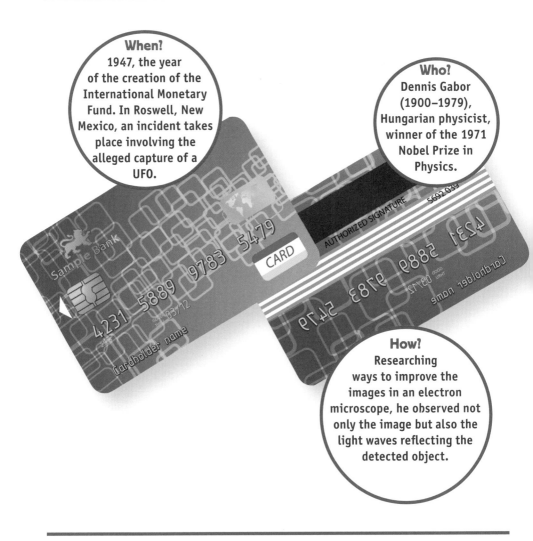

When?
1947, the year of the creation of the International Monetary Fund. In Roswell, New Mexico, an incident takes place involving the alleged capture of a UFO.

Who?
Dennis Gabor (1900–1979), Hungarian physicist, winner of the 1971 Nobel Prize in Physics.

How?
Researching ways to improve the images in an electron microscope, he observed not only the image but also the light waves reflecting the detected object.

A brilliant generation of Hungarian scientists was born between the late nineteenth and early twentieth centuries: the biophysicist Georg von Békésy, the aerospace engineer Theodore von Kármán, the computer pioneer John von Neumann, nuclear physicists Leo Szilard and Edward Teller, the physicist Eugene Wigner, and the one who concerns us now, Dennis Gabor.

Holography is mainly used for ID tags or for security, and applied to such things as credit cards, checks, passports, ID cards and tickets. This is done by inserting a flat holographic film.

Gabor came from a wealthy family in the Austro-Hungarian Empire. As a small boy, he showed that he already had the makings of an inventor. At the age of ten, he applied for his first patent: a carousel system using tethered aircraft, with an electric motor and belts that changed in elevation as they revolved around a central axis. At 23 he received a degree in electrical engineering from the Technical University of Berlin. After obtaining a Ph.D. in engineering, he began working in Berlin at Siemens and Halske AG, where he developed high-pressure mercury vapor and cadmium lamps. With Hitler's rise to power, his contract with Siemens was rescinded on account of his Jewish origin. Then he traveled to the United Kingdom, where he continued working in the field of engineering until, in 1947, he discovered, by chance, the invention that would win him international fame: the hologram.

Actually, what Gabor was looking for was a method to improve the resolution and definition in the electron microscope. His intention was to use optical means to compensate for the deficiencies of the image. To do this, he

· ·

At present holograms can be used for the art of deception, simulating actors who are just light beams, even with different colors.

· ·

3-D photography has progressed by computers being enabled to generate three-dimensional images on two-dimensional screens, but in reality these are not holograms.

created a photographic process for recording images. It involved photographing not only the object but also the light waves reflected by the object. This allows one to store large amounts of information in a small space, thanks to what is called the superposition principle. By so doing, Gabor had unwittingly generated the first hologram. It took a little while for practical applications of holograms to be recognized, but in the 1950s another technological development led to their wider use. A hologram requires a coherent light source (with phase constant oscillation), which was not available until the invention of the laser. Up until then, to achieve consistency it was necessary to use a conventional light source to filter the beams. In 1963, in the United States, Emmeth Leith and Juris Upatnieks made the first truly three-dimensional holograms.

As we know it today, holography is an advanced photographic technique used to create three-dimensional images. With the help of a laser beam, it microscopically records a photosensitive film that, when lit from the right perspective, projects an image in three dimensions.

For this discovery, Dennis Gabor received the Nobel Prize in Physics in 1971.

What's That Sound

WHAT? Cosmic Background Radiation and the Big Bang

When
1964, year that the album *Meet the Beatles* is released. The first computer program written in BASIC language is created.

Who?
The German Arno Allan Penzias and the American Robert Woodrow Wilson. Both received the Nobel Prize in Physics in 1978.

How?
While conducting a study on a new type of antenna for Bell Labs, they found a source of noise they could not explain.

The universe originated in a space-time singularity of infinite density and physical paradox.

Theory of the Big Bang

Cosmic background radiation is electromagnetic radiation that fills the universe. It is believed to be a remnant from the time of the creation of the universe, the day when photons were released.

One of the most important findings in the field of astrophysics was the result of serendipity. Let's try to put this in context. Since the early twentieth century, a lot of scientists have added their two cents to explain the Big Bang, a theory about the birth of the universe. But it was not until the accidental discovery of cosmic background radiation that scientists began to get a sense of what really happened a whopping 13.7 billion years ago (the accepted age of the universe as we know it). At that time, all the matter and energy in the universe were concentrated at a single point, a kind of hot and very dense plasma. Of course, it was a little tight inside there, and the density caused it to blow up in a gigantic explosion (the famous Big Bang). After the fireworks, the universe began to expand to reach its current state...and it continues. This Big Bang has left a clear trail, which is known as cosmic background radiation. The study of it has provided valuable information on the formation of the universe and its age. But let's return to our serendipity.

In 1964, two young engineers from Bell Labs (owned by the American telephone company AT&T) were manipulating a high sensitivity antenna in Holmdel (New Jersey). They were bothered by a series of interferences picked up by the radio receivers, but gradually managed to remove all of the background noises...except one. To their surprise, they discovered that the signal was not just isotropic (had the same appearance when measured in all directions), but also did not vary according to the day or the season. The data suggested that persistent microwave radiation could only come from one place: the so-

• •

Cosmic microwave background radiation fills up the universe. Most cosmologists consider this as proof of the Big Bang Theory.

• •

lar system. Nonetheless, Penzias and Wilson continued to believe that this was noise coming from the antenna itself. In that region, pigeons tended to perch on the antenna, soiling it with feathers and droppings. But once clean, the noise was still there. They had no idea where that signal was coming from.

Interestingly, some 30 miles away (in Princeton), a team of physicists led by Robert H. Dicke and P. J. E. Peebles were working with the intention of discovering the so-called cosmic background radiation as trace evidence of the Big Bang Theory. As chance would have it, Penzias and Wilson contacted them to ask about the origin of these waves. Hanging up the phone, Dicke concluded, "They have beaten us to it." Thanks to this accidental discovery, Penzias and Wilson were awarded the 1978 Nobel Prize in Physics.

From the Big Bang to the Big Freeze

Everything that is born, dies. It seems that this may also be the case with the universe as we know it today. Of course, in this event, all knowledge of it will be lost as well. It is predicted that this scenario will occur within 1 billion years if the universe continues to expand. What will happen? Well, most of the universe will darken completely, and it will become so cold that it will be incompatible with life, the so-called Big Freeze.

A Different Kind of Star

WHAT? Pulsars

When?
1967, the year that Louis Leakey announces the discovery of pre-human fossils. Che Guevara dies. The first heart transplant is performed.

Who?
Antony Hewish, Nobel Prize for Physics in 1974, and thesis supervisor for Jocelyn Bell who, although she was the first to detect the emission of pulsars, was not recognized at the time.

How?
Tracking space in search of radio sources and detecting a pattern in the registers of the readings while studying quasars.

A pulsar is a neutron star that rotates at a high speed, generating an intense electromagnetic field. And what is a neutron star? It is the remnant remaining after the explosion of a massive star, between 10 and 50 times larger than the Sun. Let's say that the core of the supernova is transformed into a neutron star. It looks like a big ball of solid iron and is capable of generating strong magnetic fields in space. It also emits powerful radio waves, which it launches as a compressed beam of light. Like a cosmic lighthouse, this radiation rotates at regular intervals in accordance with the rotation of the star, which can rotate several hundred times per second. This rotation reaches an incredible speed of 44,000 miles per second, generating the aforementioned magnetic fields. That said, it would seem easy to discern something this spectacular in the middle of a dark sky. That was, however, not the case. Once again serendipity played a role. It all began in the mid-1960s with the development of a technique to measure a phenomenon called Interplanetary Scintillation (IPS). This is a measure of the variations in the intensity of a distant radio signal produced by a stellar source, when captured by a radio telescope.

Neutron stars formed from massive stars are depleted and collapse. Their rapid rotation can lead to the formation of a pulsar that emits energy in space and assumes extraordinary forms, such as this dusty torus around the central section of the star.

At that time, scientists were investigating quasars, and because their frequency of scintillation is very high, IPS was perfect for this. Recognizing this, Antony Hewish of the Department of Radio Astronomy, Cambridge University, designed a large radio telescope (equivalent in size to 57 tennis courts!) and put some university students in charge of the vast amount of data received daily from outer space. Jocelyn Bell was one of these students. The young Irish woman (then 24 years old) was very meticulous in her work. She quickly detected the sought after fluctuations of quasars. But she had found something more: a strange type of signal that

Never before had a signal beyond the solar system been picked up with such precision and pulse frequency.

The constellation of Cassiopeia, one of the locations where, in 1967, signals that seemed to come from intelligent life were received but turned out to be pulsars.

fluctuated too rapidly for the capacity of the radio telescope. They then installed a new chart to record microwave bursts lasting as little as one-twentieth of a second and arriving regularly every 1.33 seconds.

The team was puzzled by the signal. Some thought the pulses were being emitted by an intelligent civilization of extraterrestrial origin. In fact, they named the signal LGM-1 (Little Green Men), a clear reference to their initial suspicions. The discovery was a revelation. Never before had a signal from beyond the solar system been picked up with such precision and pulse repitition frequency. At first, they decided to be cautious and not announce their discovery. In addition, the media at that time was very responsive to reports of extraterrestrial sightings, and they were afraid of alarming the public. They continued analyzing the signal and even detected new sources (particularly from the constellation Cassiopeia). Finally, they concluded that the signal was the result of a natural phenomenon, and in February, 1968, Hewish made the official announcement of the discovery of pulsating astronomical radio sources, or pulsars.

But the question remained as to the origin of this type of signal and how these precise bursts of energy were being generated. These issues were under discussion in the scientific community when the astrophysicists Thomas Gold of Austria and Fred Hoyle of Great Britain proposed that these signals do not come from ordinary stars, but from the so-called neutron stars. In consequence of rapid rotation, they emit narrow beams of electromagnetic radiation in the form of radio waves.

For the discovery of the first pulsar, Antony Hewish was awarded the Nobel Prize for Physics in 1974. His assistant, Jocelyn Bell, received no recognition, despite being the first to identify the radio signal. This notwithstanding, during her career she has accumulated many prestigious awards: the Michelson Medal, J. Robert Oppenheimer Memorial Prize, Beatrice M. Tinsley Prize and the Herschel Medal of the Royal Astronomical Society.

Currently, more than 600 pulsars are known. There are several types: X-Ray pulsars, rotation-powered pulsars, including those that emit only gamma rays, and magnetars (aged pulsars with very weak signals, but with extreme rotation speeds).

Radio telescope used for observation of space. The large parabolic antenna detects radiation emitted by pulsars.

The most famous pulsar

One of the most famous pulsars is found in the center of what is known as the Crab Nebula, which is 6,300 light years from Earth. It is the remnant of a supernova that was observed and documented on July 4, 1054 by Chinese and Arab astronomers.

In fact, the magnitude of the explosion was such that it was visible in broad daylight for almost two years. In the center of this spectacular nebula is PSR 0531+121. This was one of the first pulsars discovered back in 1968. Its estimated diameter is 30 km, and it emits pulses of radiation every 33 milliseconds. The energy released by this pulsar is enormous and is partly responsible for the high brightness of the nebula, which is 75,000 times greater than the Sun.

Crab Nebula, where one of the most famous pulsars, the PSR 0531+121, is found. It rotates around itself at 30 revolutions per minute.

Warning! Unidentified Shining Object

WHAT? Gamma Rays from Outer Space

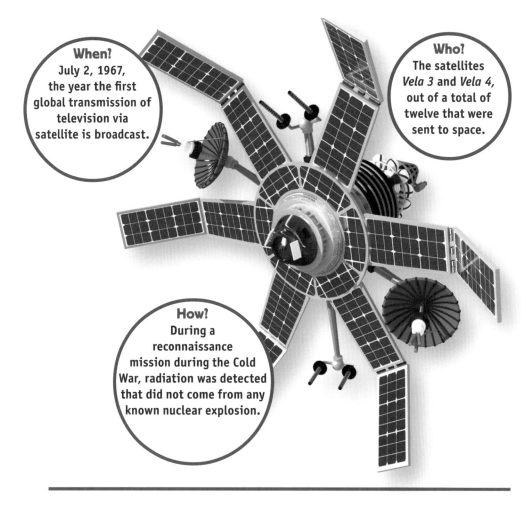

When!
July 2, 1967, the year the first global transmission of television via satellite is broadcast.

Who!
The satellites *Vela 3* and *Vela 4*, out of a total of twelve that were sent to space.

How!
During a reconnaissance mission during the Cold War, radiation was detected that did not come from any known nuclear explosion.

· ·

At first, scientists considered the possibility that they came from an extraterrestrial civilization, but soon they realized that they had stumbled upon a new cosmic phenomenon.

· ·

During the Cold War, the United States created the so-called Vela Project, intended to monitor nuclear explosions from tests carried out by the enemy on the other side of the Iron Curtain. According to the Limited Test Ban Treaty of 1963, all nuclear test explosions were banned except for those performed underground.

Developed by the Defense Advanced Research Projects Agency (DARPA) and supervised by the U.S. Air Force, this project consisted of three elements:

- Vela Uniform. Methods and systems for detecting underground nuclear explosions.
- Vela Sierra. Methods for detecting nuclear explosions in the atmosphere. It had six surveillance satellites.
- Vela Hotel. Methods for detecting nuclear signals from space. It also had six surveillance satellites.

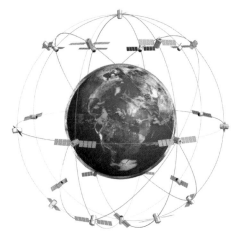

These satellites were fitted with sensors capable of capturing nuclear explosions at distances of about 5,000 kilometers. Such explosions produce a unique signal: a flash and an intense blaze that lasts about 1 millisecond, followed by a second light emission that is longer and less intense. The satellites were being used for this purpose when they unexpectedly

Using communications satellites, it is possible to detect nuclear explosions, even deep underground.

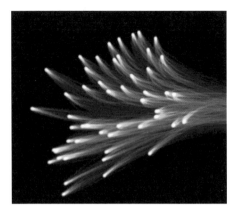

Gamma rays are produced by violent phenomena such as supernova explosions, and do not pass through the atmosphere.

began to detect a mysterious emission of gamma rays that were not from Earth. There was, at first, speculation that these came from an extraterrestrial civilization, but it was soon realized that it had to do with gamma rays originating in space.

Gamma rays are a form of high energy electromagnetic radiation. They consist of photons (carrier particles of all forms of electromagnetic radiation) produced in a subatomic process, such as the decay of a positron-electron pair. (The positron is the antiparticle of the electron, and their union signifies its transformation into energy.) They are generated, for example, in a nuclear explosion and can penetrate deeply into matter. Until 1967, it was believed that they could only be found on Earth, but the Vela satellites discovered that they form part of the cosmic rays that bombard Earth from space.

The discovery by the Vela satellites of sources of radiation outside the solar system was published in *The Astrophysical Journal* in 1973 under the title "Observations of Gamma-Ray Bursts of Cosmic Origin."

Now You See Them, Now You Don't

WHAT? The Rings of Uranus

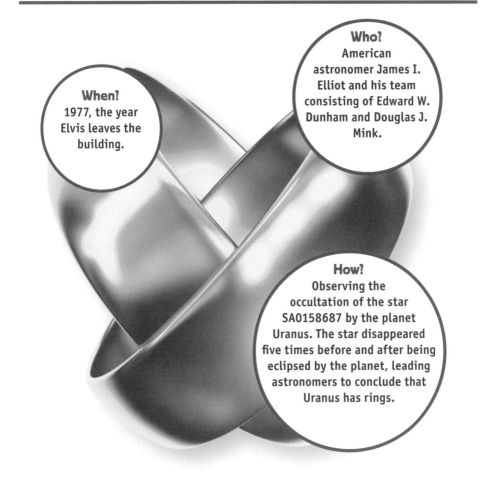

When?
1977, the year Elvis leaves the building.

Who?
American astronomer James I. Elliot and his team consisting of Edward W. Dunham and Douglas J. Mink.

How?
Observing the occultation of the star SAO158687 by the planet Uranus. The star disappeared five times before and after being eclipsed by the planet, leading astronomers to conclude that Uranus has rings.

William Herschel, portrayed in 1785 by Lemuel Francis Abbott. The great German scientist discovered the seventh planet of the solar system in 1781. He named the planet "The Georgian Star," in honor of the king of England, who appointed him Court Astronomer. In the early nineteenth century, it was renamed Uranus, father of Jupiter in classical mythology.

Z, 6, 5, 4, a, b, h, g, d, l, e, n, m, might seem like a secret code from the old KGB or an encrypted message from an alien civilization. In fact, this strange list of numbers and letters is nothing other than the names of the 13 rings encircling the planet Uranus (in ascending order). Relatively young rings are "only" 600 million years old, with radii ranging from 38,000 km of Zeta (z) and 98,000 km of E (m). The rings are thought to have originated following the collision of several satellites orbiting around the seventh planet of the solar system.

To find the first documentation of their existence, we must go back to the eighteenth century, when the German astronomer William Herschel (who discovered the planet Uranus) wrote in his notebook the following annotation: "Feb. 22, 1789. A ring was suspected." He drew a small diagram of the ring and even provided information on its brightness and color. These notes were published in the prestigious *Philosophical Transactions of the Royal Society*. But for the next chapter of the story we need to leap forward in time two hundred years.

In 1977, a number of observatories proposed the launch of an international campaign to observe a phenomenon much loved by astronomers: stellar occultation. In this case, they focused their telescopes toward the star SA0158687, which, back then, was going to be occulted by the planet Uranus. The idea was to study the atmosphere of the distant planet by analyzing the variation of light from the star. One of the participants was the Kuiper Airborne Observatory (KAO), which had a telescope mounted on a modified transport aircraft

* *

Instead of darkening in a regular manner, the light of SA0158687 decreased in intensity for a few seconds and then illuminated again..

* *

capable of reaching an altitude of up to 45,000 feet (14 km). The team responsible for the study comprised the Americans James I. Elliot, Edward W. Dunham and Douglas J. Mink.

They quickly discovered that something unusual was happening in the occulted star. Instead of darkening in a regular manner, the light of SA0158687 decreased in intensity for a few seconds and then illuminated again. This phenomenon was repeated on five occasions before the final occultation (which lasted about 25 minutes). Furthermore, in some cases, those time intervals were almost symmetrical.

The conclusion they came to is one of the most famous astronomical serendipities in history: the only possible cause could be the presence of rings around Uranus. These first five events of occultation were named with the Greek letters α, β, γ, δ and ε. But later more rings were found, two of them from the *Voyager 2* spacecraft, which flew by Uranus in January 1986.

The thirteen rings of Uranus can be divided into three groups: nine narrow main rings, two dusty rings and two outer rings. All consist mainly of macroscopic particles and dust.

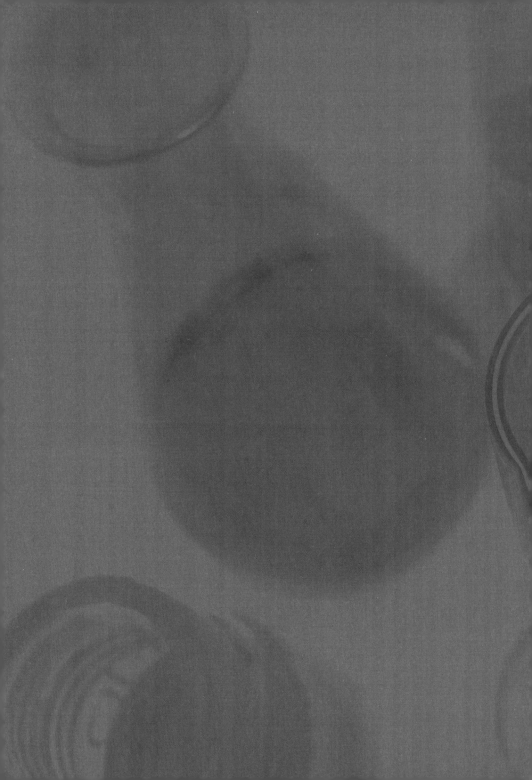

Great Historical Coincidences:

CHEMISTRY

The Mouse that Lived Longer than Expected

WHAT? Oxygen

When?
1774, the year that Louis XVI of France ascends the throne.

Who?
Joseph Priestley (1733–1804), although it has also been attributed to Carl Wilhelm Scheele and Antoine Lavoisier.

How?
By checking the respiration of a mouse in a hermetically sealed environment.

Almost 21 percent of Earth's atmosphere is oxygen, an essential element for the development of life on Earth. At the dawn of time, the primitive Earth's atmosphere was composed primarily of water (H_2O) and carbon dioxide (CO_2). The oxygen element came later, probably due to the hydrolysis (a chemical reaction that occurs between water and other substances) of water caused by solar radiation. Marine algae also did their part, increasing the amount of oxygen in the atmosphere via photosynthetic activity. That enabled the stratospheric ozone layer to form, facilitating the evolution of terrestrial life.

Oxygen, a colorless, odorless and tasteless gas, was discovered by chance thanks to the collaboration of...a mouse! But let's take it one step at a time. A few years before this serendipitous find, between 1770 and 1773, the Swedish chemist Carl Wilhelm Scheele was the first to generate oxygen, which he called "air of fire." He did it by heating manganese dioxide (pyrolusite) with concentrated sulfuric acid (oil of vitriol). These were the days before the Chemical Revolution, and the so-called phlogiston theory was dominant. Now discredited, this theory argued that metals and generally all combustible substances contain a weightless substance, which was named phlogiston. It was believed that upon combustion of any substance, phlogiston separated as flames, leaving behind an incombustible residue.

Accepting this theory, many chemists considered phlogiston to be a material substance. This meant, for exam-

Oxygen is predominant in the biosphere, all the regions on Earth and its surrounding area that sustain living organisms.

Priestley knew from previous experiments that a mouse could survive in a sealed container for up to 15 minutes. He was completely astonished when the animal held out without suffocating twice as long in the new dephlogisticated air.

ple, that during the combustion of any material, they thought that flames oscillated because phlogiston was being released. According to this belief, such things as rust, calcination, and the transformation by oxidation of a metal to its mineral or lime, were all considered products created by the release of phlogiston.

The English chemist Joseph Priestley also adhered to this erroneous theory. In 1774, he used a magnifying glass to concentrate sunlight to heat mercuric oxide inside a bell jar. Priestley himself described the experiment in his series of volumes entitled *Experiments and Observations on Different Kinds of Air*:

Having procured a lens of twelve inches in diameter, and twenty inches focal distance, I proceeded with great alacrity to examine, by the help of it, to discover what kind of air a great variety of substances, natural and factitious, would yield, putting them into the vessel, which I filled with quick-silver, and kept inverted in a basin of the same. . . .

With this apparatus, after a variety of experiments, . . . on the first of August, 1774, I endeavored to extract air from mercurius calcinatus per se; I presently found that, by means of this lens, air was expelled from it very readily. Having got about three or four times as much as the bulk of my materials, I admitted water into it, and found that it was not imbibed by it. But what sur-

Portrait of Joseph Priestley, by Ellen Sharples, in 1794. Priestley was a scientist, cleric, theologian, philosopher and educator. He discovered several gases and invented soda water. He lost some of his prestige because of his hypothesis of phlogiston, which was associated with alchemy.

prised me more than I can express was that a candle burned in this air with a remarkable vigorous flame, very much like that enlarged flame . . . I was utterly at a loss to account for it.

Priestley had isolated oxygen but had no idea what he had discovered. Of course, he baptized it with a resounding name: dephlogisticated air. His experiments showed him that objects burned better in its presence. This led him to conclude that the gas was able to absorb more phlogiston than burning objects.

And now we come to the mouse in question. Priestley continued to experiment with the new gas. On March 8, 1775, he introduced an adult mouse into a sealed container of the new "air." The scientist knew from previous experiments that a mouse could survive in similar conditions for up to fifteen minutes. Much to his surprise ,the animal survived without choking twice as long. He continued introducing mice and finally concluded that this new gas was perfectly breathable, although at 100% it is very toxic.

The third and final player in this story about the discovery of oxygen is Antoine-Laurent Lavoisier. This chemist from France, considered the father of modern chemistry, demolished the false concept of phlogiston and oxygen, being the first to publish a paper on this gas.

Heating mercuric oxide Priestley obtained two gases; one of them was mercury, which condensed into droplets, but the other was unknown. He isolated it in a container and made several experiments. Wood caught fire and burned easily, and mice became very active. He breathed it in and felt its invigorating effect. He had discovered oxygen.

Purely by Chance

WHAT? Urea

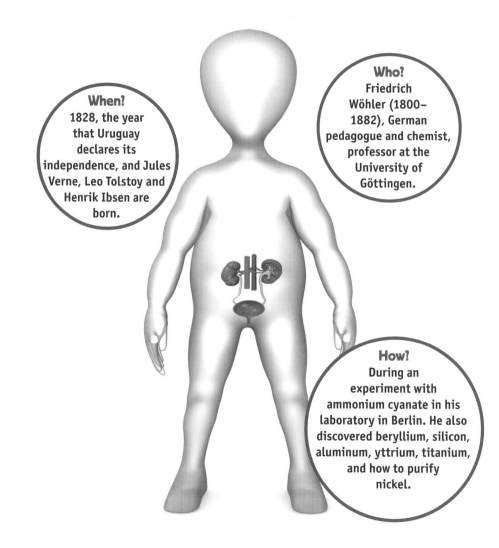

When?
1828, the year that Uruguay declares its independence, and Jules Verne, Leo Tolstoy and Henrik Ibsen are born.

Who?
Friedrich Wöhler (1800–1882), German pedagogue and chemist, professor at the University of Göttingen.

How?
During an experiment with ammonium cyanate in his laboratory in Berlin. He also discovered beryllium, silicon, aluminum, yttrium, titanium, and how to purify nickel.

I can now say that I can make urea without the involve-
ment of an animal kidney, whether from a man or a dog.

Friedrich Wöhler in a letter to his mentor, the
Swedish chemist Jöns Jacob Berzelius.

The French chemist Lavoisier had disproved the contro-
versial phlogiston theory. Before being guillotined in yet
another bloody French revolution, he showed that the
combustion process was not due to the issuance of phlogiston but to the incorporation of oxygen. It was the
dawn of modern chemistry.

The subject of combustion being resolved, another scientific debate arose when, in the late eighteenth century, vitalism arrived on the scene. This theory posited the
existence of a force, or vital impulse, without which life
could not be explained. All living organisms possessed this
vital force, which distinguished them from inert matter.
According to the vitalists, only living organisms could produce organic matter.

All beautiful theories are, however, subject to a few ugly
facts, and vitalism was doomed by an accidental discovery
by the German chemist Friedrich Wöhler. The scientist's
finding demonstrated that it was indeed possible to artificially obtain a chemical product created by life itself.

Organic chemistry came into existence on the day when
Wöhler managed to artificially synthesize urea (present
in the urine of animals and humans). It must, however,
be admitted that he did not intend to initiate this new
field of scientific endeavor. One day in 1828, Wöhler was
in his laboratory at the Polytechnic School in Berlin. He
had obtained ammonium cyanate by mixing hot lead cyanate with ammonia, and he was boiling it in order to crys-
tallize it. That was when the chemist observed the formation of large colorless crystals that did not correspond with

Friedrich Wöhler demonstrated
that the product resulting
from a vital function could
be obtained from inorganic
matter. During his long
career as a researcher, he
also isolated aluminum and
beryllium and discovered
ammonium oxalate.

. . . .

The science of that era still held that a vital force apart from matter animated living organisms.

. . . .

ammonium cyanate.

He analyzed the crystals and, to his surprise, confirmed that it was urea. Unintentionally, Wöhler had transformed an inorganic element into an organic one. Goodbye vitalism! The surprise discovery created a big stir. It was the beginning of organic chemistry.

In fact, Wöhler had not actually synthesized an organic compound, but transformed an inorganic compound. The first real synthesis of an organic compound (no serendipity) should be credited to Adolph W. H. Kolbe, a disciple of Wöhler. In 1845, Kolbe synthesized acetic acid.

But this inspired several researchers to expand on his research with the aim of being able to emulate nature for the benefit of industry. This led to the invention of all sorts of things, such as plastic and artificial fertilizers.

The discovery as recounted by Wöhler

By the action of cyanogen [C2N2] in liquid ammonia are formed, among other products, oxalic acid and a white crystallized substance which is not ammonium cyanate, but which is always obtained by combining cyanic acid and ammonia. The fact that combining these substances seems to change their nature and render them into a new form returned my attention to this topic. My investigation showed the unexpected result that cyanic acid combined with ammonia is urea. This is a remarkable fact because it provides an example of an organic substance artificially produced from inorganic substances.

Annalen der Physik und Chemie (1828)

A Big Bounce

WHAT? Vulcanization

When?
1839, the year Faraday explains the true nature of electricity. The first Opium War breaks out in China.

Who?
Charles Goodyear (1800–1860), with no formal training, a descendant of one of the founders of the colony of New Haven in 1638.

How?
When natural rubber mixed with sulfur was dropped accidentally on the stove in his laboratory. However, much earlier, Mayans and Aztecs used sulfur to stabilize the rubber used in their ball games. Their method, however, had been forgotten. Goodyear spent five years trying to stabilize rubber.

The Goodyear Company, founded by Frank Seiberling, was named in honor of the discoverer of the rubber vulcanization process.

Rubber is collected from an incision in the bark. The liquid obtained is treated with acid to incorporate sulfur. But this form of production from a tree is now only done in a few places, such as Cambodia, and is primarily sold for handicrafts.

Pneumatic tires, waterproof items, insulators, adhesives...With its excellent properties of elasticity and resistance, rubber has a multitude of uses. These properties were already known in Mesoamerican civilizations more than 3,000 years ago. At that time, a ritual game was played with balls made with this material. In fact, in 1989, a team of archeologists from the National Institute of Anthropology and History (INAH) of Mexico found 12 rubber balls in perfect condition at a site in Veracruz.

When the Spanish arrived in America, they took careful note of rubber and, before long, it was introduced in Europe. But they did not have much success with its application. Rubber soon fell into oblivion until, in 1731, France sent geographer and naturalist Charles Marie de la Condamine to America. Five years later, the French sent back several rolls of crude rubber, together with a description of the products manufactured with the material by Amazonian Indians.

In this way, interest in rubber was revived, and many began to work on its possible applications. One of the first to distinguish himself was Joseph Priestley. In 1770, the English chemist discovered that rubber could be used to erase writing written with a pencil on paper. He had just invented the eraser. More applications followed from there: for example, footwear, clothing, mail sacks and covered wagons. But an unsolved problem still remained: over time rubber (being a natural substance) is damaged by sunlight and other weathering agents. It gets sticky in the summer, and crumbles in the winter.

There were many who experimented with rubber and tested various possibilities without success. This was until one of them, Charles Goodyear, had an incredible stroke of luck. In 1839, Goodyear was experimenting in his laboratory with a mixture of natural rubber and sulfur, when some of it accidentally spilled onto the stove. After cleaning up the mess, Goodyear ignored the debris, and left it in a corner of the lab. The next day, he was astonished to find that the charred rubber had acquired an unexpected hardness, was waterproof and retained an obvious elasticity. By accident, he had just discovered the vulcanization process (named in honor of the Roman god Vulcan).

Charles Marie de la Condamine, French geographer and explorer, was the first to send samples of rubber to Europe.

Why erasers erase

After arriving in Europe, one of the first astonishing uses for rubber was as an eraser. But have you ever stopped to wonder why an eraser erases? Well, here is the explanation: when we write in pencil on paper, charcoal remains on the surface of the page. This is caused by adhesion, an electromagnetic force operating between interactive molecules of different compositions. There is nothing better than rubber to break this bond. It has a stronger force of adhesion than the paper to which the charcoal is adhered. In addition, the eraser also contains sulfur and vegetable oils that help remove dirt particles. Nowadays, erasers contain a synthetic derivative of rubber, which is very similar to the natural type.

Apollo in the Forge of Vulcan by Velásquez. Vulcan was the god of blacksmiths, and the vulcanization process was named after him.

Instead of rushing to patent his discovery, Goodyear waited until a few years later. By the time he finally decided to do it, the English scientist and engineer Thomas Hancock had already beaten him to it in Europe. In fact, the famous Goodyear Tire & Rubber Company, founded in 1898, has nothing to do with the discoverer of vulcanization. Charles Goodyear never made money with his discovery and died completely broke.

In the Dark Room

WHAT? The Daguerreotype

When?
1835, the year the island of Concepción in Chile is destroyed by an earthquake. *The Beagle*, with Darwin on board, stops at the Galapagos Islands.

Who?
Frenchman Louis Daguerre (1787–1851), painter and stage designer, first to popularize photography.

How?
By casually placing a photographic plate inside the same cabinet where there was mercury. A few days later, he discovered that there was an image. He sold the process to the French government in 1839.

From today onwards, we are able to travel without moving.

From an article published in the journal *La Lumière* in 1839

Louis Daguerre began as an architect, learned to draw and worked as an assistant to an important stage designer for theater and opera. He was also a painter, a trade in which he emphasized perspective, and finally went down in history as the inventor of the diorama. Below, his diorama of a railway station.

The birth of photography is also due in part to a chance discovery. Between the sixteenth and seventeenth centuries, various versions of the camera obscura, the forerunner of today's camera, were created. The term "camera obscura" was coined by Johannes Kepler in 1604. Little by little, sucessive inventions would lead to a primitive camera. But discovering the process of fixing an image by means of light was still a long way off.

The German scientist Johann H. Schulze made the first successful attempt at creating a light-sensitive substance. In 1727, he found that silver salts were blackened by the effect of light. But it was Thomas Wedgwood who first applied these compounds to a surface, leather in particular. The great dilemma, however, was not to capture an image, but how to fix it permanently. Joseph N. Niépce was working on this in his laboratory in the French countryside. An enthusiast of lithography, the chemist used a camera obscura and silver salts with the aim of obtaining fixed images. In his first attempt, he tried fixing an image on stone. He continued with paper and glass, and even tried metals, such as tin and copper. As he wrote, his endeavor was "to discover in the emanations of the luminous fluid an agent susceptible to impression, exactly and durably, images transmitted by an optical method, and to obtain a mark that is not altered excessively rapidly."

His dream was realized in 1816, when he obtained the first photographic images in history, but none of them is preserved. They were negative images on paper. But ignoring the possibility of turning them into positive images, he eventually abandoned the project. A few years later, he tried again. This time he obtained positive images directly. He called reproductions of already existing engravings "heliographs," and images taken directly from life by the camera "views." In fact, the first known photograph in history, entitled *View from the Window at Le Gras*, dated 1826, is now held in the collection of the University of Texas.

Niépce's experiments came to the attention of the painter Jean Louis-Jacques-Mandé Daguerre, who was also after the same thing: to obtain fixed images and sell the patent. Initially, Niépce did not pay much attention to Daguerre's commercial aspirations, but he did begin to associate with him. On December 5, 1829, they signed a partnership agreement in which Daguerre recognized that Niépce "had found a new method of fixing, without resorting to drawing, the views offered by nature." Working separately, while keeping each other abreast of their progress, they continued to work on plates made from copper, silver and crystal.

Niépce died in 1833. Daguerre continued to experiment, and two years later an accident happened that would change the history of photography. Tired of trying items that did not give any results, Daguerre placed a plate impressed with a latent image (a faint image) in a cabinet where there were various chemical products. He left it under lock and key and forgot about it. The next day, he opened it and discovered that there was a clear and sharp image on the plate. Which substance had provoked the miracle? Inside there were too many to figure it out at first. So he went about removing the products one by one, checking that the plates still appeared sharp, until he withdrew a vial of mercury. At last he had found what he had spent years searching for: mercury vapor was able to fix the image onto the

View from the Window at Le Gras (Point de vue du Gras) is the oldest preserved photograph. Joseph Nicéphore Niépce took it in 1827, from a third-floor window of his house in Saint-Loup-de-Varennes in Burgundy.

plate. It was the birth of the daguerreotype (which, of course, he named after himself), the predecessor to modern photography.

In 1839, the French government purchased his invention, ensuring Daguerre an annual pension of 6,000 francs. The invention was officially presented at the French Academy of Sciences in Paris and, in this way, Daguerre succeeded, thanks to serendipity, in going down in history as one of the fathers of photography, along with Joseph N. Niépce.

View of the Boulevard du Temple, Paris. This daguerreotype of 1838 contains the first human beings ever photographed. The exposure exceeded ten minutes, and the carriages went by too fast to appear. Only the two men near the bottom left of the photograph, one polishing the other's shoes, are visible.

In Living Color

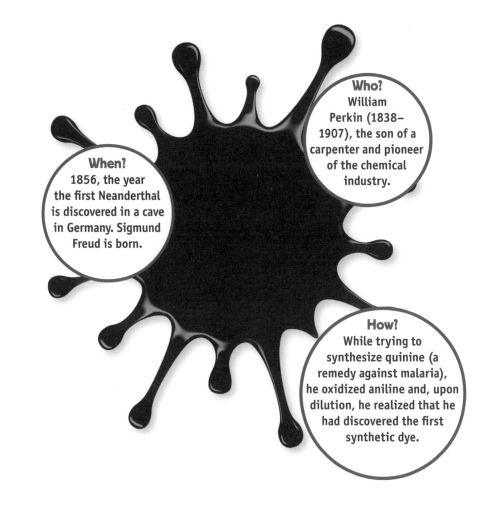

Who?
William Perkin (1838–1907), the son of a carpenter and pioneer of the chemical industry.

When?
1856, the year the first Neanderthal is discovered in a cave in Germany. Sigmund Freud is born.

How?
While trying to synthesize quinine (a remedy against malaria), he oxidized aniline and, upon dilution, he realized that he had discovered the first synthetic dye.

Above, August Wilhelm von Hofmann, who was trying to synthesize quinine in his lab with the help of William Perkin (below), who, one day when Hoffman was absent, tested a method he had devised and, by chance, discovered aniline.

If your discovery does not make the fabric too expensive, it is definitely one of the most valuable that has emerged in a long time..

Pullar Brothers, Dyers of Perth, Australia

In the late nineteenth and early twentieth centuries, European colonies suffered the scourge of malaria. Renowned chemists sought the possibility of synthesizing quinine. This natural compound was utilized for its antimalarial properties, but its extraction (from the cinchona tree) was slow and costly. So it would be best to find a way to manufacture quinine artificially. The famous German chemist August Wilhelm von Hofmann was working on it, focusing his work on coal tar in his laboratory at the Royal College of Chemistry in London. This black and thick liquid was available very cheaply as a by-product of the growing gas industry. It was already known that this substance could be treated with nitric acid to form a yellowish oily substance called nitrobenzene. By reducing it, one could also obtain aniline, so named because it is prepared initially from a basis of indigo. Hofmann arrived at a method for making aniline more cheaply and in large quantities. But what the chemist had wanted to develop was quinine, working from certain derivatives of hydrocarbons, such as naphthalene and benzene.

Among Hofmann's students, an eighteen-year-old youth named William Perkin stood out. He also was excited by the idea of synthesizing quinine, and conduct-

Perkin was about to toss the test tube when he noticed that some purplish streaks had begun to dye the solution completely.

ed experiments on his own. With the aim of obtaining synthetic quinine, it first occurred to him to oxidize N-Ethyl-o-toluidine, a derivative of aniline, with potassium dichromate. This failed, and he tried it again with aniline. It was the Easter vacation of 1856, and in his home laboratory the blackish precipitate that appeared in the test tube had really awful spots. He was about to discard it, when he noticed that some purplish streaks had begun to dye the solution completely. By the grace of serendipity, he had just invented the first synthetic dye, mauveine, or Perkin's mauve, named in his honor.

China aster (*Callistephus*) has a color remarkably similar to the first artificial dye, more commonly known as purple aniline, mauveine, or mauve. It was synthesized by William Henry Perkin on Easter Day, 1856, when, while oxidizing aniline sulfate in search of a remedy for malaria, he obtained a precipitate which when dissolved in alcohol, offered this splendid purple.

The young Englishman began experimenting and found that he could dye silk a bright mauve that was resistant to light, and held up well in the wash. Perkin sent a sample of this dyed silk to the Pullar brothers, dyers at Perth. Their reply could not have been more encouraging. "If your discovery does not make the fabric too expensive, it is definitely one of the most valuable that has emerged in a long time." Without thinking twice, Perkin rushed to patent his purple dye. This is how he described the formula for his stunning synthetic dye:

I take cold solution of sulphate of aniline, or cold solution of sulphate of toluidine, or cold solution of sulphate of xylidine, or cold solution of sulphate of cumidine, or mixture of any one of such solutions with any others or other of them, and as much of cold solution of soluble bichromate as contains base enough to convert the sulphuric acid in any of the above-mentioned solutions into a neutral sulfate. I then mix the solutions . . . and digest it repeatedly with coal-tar naptha.

That serendipity would make him a millionaire. In those days, mauve had been prized by the nobility, and Perkin's dye quickly popularized it. In fact, Perkin's mauve traded at the same price as platinum. At the age of 21, Perkin already had a factory running at full capacity and was responsible for commercial tasks, such as making technical improvements in the industrial dyeing process. Perkin recounted his discovery: "I was endeavouring to convert an artificial base into the natural alkaloid quinine, but my experiment, instead of yielding the colourless quinine, gave a reddish powder." After using aniline, a simple base, he obtained a perfectly black product. "This when purified, and digested with spirits-of-wine, gave the mauve dye."

Perkin's discovery heralded the launch of other new laboratories that manufactured dyes. In fact, it is said that it gave a big boost to the German chemical dyeing industry, which would turn the country into one of Europe's main economic engines.

One must remember that the first known organic dye was obtained from the shell of an American cochineal, the Dactylopius coccus. It was used by the Paracas culture two thousand years ago.

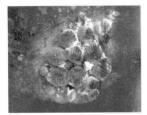

Above *Dactylopius coccus*, also called cochineal carmine, on a stalk of *Opuntia*, which is farmed, in some places, to obtain red dye.

Cut!

WHAT? Celluloid

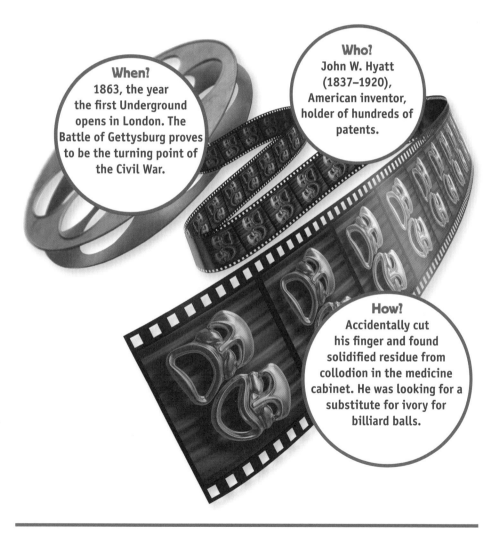

When?
1863, the year the first Underground opens in London. The Battle of Gettysburg proves to be the turning point of the Civil War.

Who?
John W. Hyatt (1837–1920), American inventor, holder of hundreds of patents.

How?
Accidentally cut his finger and found solidified residue from collodion in the medicine cabinet. He was looking for a substitute for ivory for billiard balls.

Celluloid, a flexible and transparent plastic material, is obtained by uniting nitrocellulose and camphor. But it was not until 1940 that the switch to using cellulose triacetate film reduced the risk of fire in theaters.

When he opened the drawer, he found that a bottle of collodion had spilled, forming a transparent film.

Some of the most important discoveries in the history of mankind are not the fruit of only one coincidence, but of several. Such was the case of the fortuitous discovery of the process for producing celluloid (cellulose nitrate), the first synthetic plastic, discovered in 1863 by the American John Wesley Hyatt.

It all began in 1860, when Phelan & Collander, manufacturer of billiard balls, announced a competition. In those days, billiard balls were made of ivory, a raw material that was extremely expensive to procure, as it required the hunting and killing of thousands of elephants. This was bad news for the American company, so they decided to mobilize the country's inventors to exercise their gray matter and come up with a feasible alternative to ivory. The invitation was enticing, as the winning idea would receive a prize of $10,000 (a fortune in those days). This reached the ears of an ambitious young man, John W. Hyatt, who could barely make ends meet with his work as a printer. Hyatt was not a chemist. He hadn't even studied very much, but he launched into experimentation with enthusiasm.

Hyatt couldn't come up with the exact formula to win the coveted prize. Then a lucky accident happened during one of his experiments. While handling instruments in his home laboratory, Hyatt cut his finger and ran to the medicine cabinet to dress the wound. Upon opening it, he found that the bottle of collodion (used at the time as an antiseptic) had spilled. A small amount remained on the shelf, solidified, as the solvent that contained it had evaporated. This was cellulose nitrate, and it appeared solid and flexible. Hyatt continued to experiment with this substance, and when he mixed it with camphor, he found that it acquired a very hard texture. He subjected it to heat and melted it again. Celluloid had just been invented, the first synthetic plastic in history. Years

. . . .

The first person to discover celluloid was the Englishman Alexander Parkes in 1855, but his company went bankrupt, and he could not take advantage of it. In the 1860s, Hyatt acquired the patent.

. . . .

later, Hyatt recounted:

> From my earliest experiments in nitrocellulose, incited by accidentally finding a dried bit of collodian the size and thickness of my thumb-nail, and by my very earnest efforts to find a substitute for ivory billiard balls, it was appar-ent that a semi-liquid solution of nitrocellu-lose, three-fourths of the bulk of which was a volatile liquid while the final solid was less than one-fourth the mass of the original mixture, was far from being adapted to the manufacture of solid articles, and that I must initially produce a solid solution by mechan-ical means.

Plume House, where the American Episcopal priest Hannibal Goodwin made his discovery in 1887. Goodwin patented a method of using celluloid as a backing for cinema film. However, for ten years he had to struggle with Eastman Kodak to recognize his patent.

This flexible, transparent and moisture-resistant ma-terial had numerous industrial applications. In 1887, Hannibal Williston Goodwin first used it as a backing for photographic film, thus revolutionizing the field of pho-tography and opening the way for the birth of cinema. For this reason, cinema came to be popularly known as "celluloid." Other uses for celluloid include toys, sanitary ware and various household items.

When Chemists Dream

WHAT? The Molecular Structure of Benzene

When?
1865, the year the Civil War ends and Abraham Lincoln is assassinated. Mendel proposes the laws of genetics.

Who?
August Kekulé (1829–1896), German chemist, a descendant of the Bohemian aristocracy, and amateur botanist with a gift for languages.

How?
According to him, after a dream that featured snakes biting their tails, as well as years of study on the nature of carbon bonds.

*Let us learn to dream, so we can find the truth. But let us
be beware of publishing our dreams until they have been
tested by the understanding upon awakening*

August Kekulé

Benzene is an aromatic hydrocarbon, a colorless liquid
that is toxic and flammable. A good solvent of organic
substances, it is used for making such things as plastics,
explosives, dyes and medicines. This substance was discovered in 1825 by the English scientist Michael Faraday.
In the early nineteenth century, the lighting in London
houses worked with gas. The gas was obtained from natural sources, such as the fat of marine animals. It was
distributed in iron bottles and usually kept in the basement of residences. During the winter months, the extreme cold in the city caused the gas to lose some of its
capacity to burn. The owners of a factory that manufactured the gas sought Faraday's advice. He concluded that
when burned, the substance that produced the flame accumulated in the bottom of the bottles because of the
cold. In doing so, a layer of clear liquid was formed. On
analysis, Faraday discovered that it was a new hydrocarbon that a few years later (1834) would be synthesized
by the German chemist Eilhard Mitscherlich from benzo-
in resin, hence the name "benzene."

But the discovery of benzene and its molecular for-
mulation (C_6H_6) brought with it an enigma that would
take years for scientists to resolve. It was known that
its structure contained six carbon atoms and six hydrogen atoms, but no one had arrived at their exact distribution.

Picasso used to say that inspiration comes from working. And it sometimes happens that a revelation comes
when we least expect it, and in the most unusual circumstances. For example, Einstein claimed that his main

Michael Faraday (1842) by
Thomas Phillips. Faraday had
discovered electromagnetic
induction in 1831 and was
the creator of the theory of
lines of force to represent
magnetic fields. Among his
many contributions to science
is the discovery of benzene
in 1825, by isolating it from
coal gas.

. . . .

The snake that appeared in a strange dream was what inspired Kekulé to come up with the unique molecular structure of benzene.

. . . .

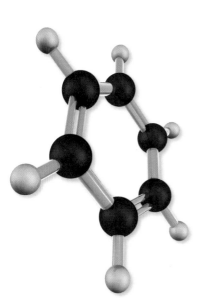

A model of a benzene molecule, a polyunsaturated aromatic hydrocarbon through a hexagon-shaped ring containing a carbon atom at each vertex, with two valences bonded by the neighboring atom and by a third to a hydrogen atom.

scientific theories came when he was sick. But for the scientist who finally discovered the structure of benzene, the muses came to him while he was sleeping. No one could figure out its structure and molecular behavior until August Kekulé, a German professor of chemistry, unconsciously came across the solution. Years later (1890), in a commemorative address on the 25th anniversary of the benzene ring theory, Kekulé himself recounted the moment:

During my stay in Ghent, I lived on the main street in an elegant residence for singles. My office overlooked a narrow side street, and daylight did not enter. For a chemist who spends many hours a day in the laboratory, this was not inconvenient at all. I was sitting, writing my textbook, although the work was not progressing because my thoughts were elsewhere. I turned my chair to the fire and sank into dreams. Again the atoms began to dance before my eyes, but this time the smaller groups remained shyly in the background. My mind's eye, sharper due to repeated visions of this kind, could now distinguish larger structures and multiple configurations, long rows sometimes fitted more closely together, and all of them coiling and braiding like snakes. What was it? One of the snakes was biting its tail, and mockingly revolved into view. As if struck by lightening, I woke up and I spent the rest of the night deducing the meaning of those visions.

These visions took shape. In 1865, Kekulé hypothesized that six carbon atoms were located at the vertices of a regular hexagon, with a hydrogen atom attached to each carbon atom. The snake in his dream had inspired Kekulé to discover the unique molecular structure of benzene. His theory created quite a stir. At the time, only linear molecular structures were known, and this ring-shaped structure was unthinkable. At that time, it was technically impossible to prove Kekulé's theory; it would take years to confirm its validity, thanks to advances in organic chemistry.

It was the American chemist Linus Pauling, holder of the 1954 Nobel Prize in Chemistry for his description of the nature of chemical bonds, who found a way to represent this behavior by superimposing the two structures developed by Kekulé. Pauling also received the Nobel Peace Prize in 1962 for his opposition to nuclear tests. He had been one of the most astute thinkers in the world of science, was one of the first quantum chemists, and made discoveries in organic and inorganic chemistry, metallurgy, psychology, immunology and anesthesiology, among others. His most important work is *The Nature of the Chemical Bond,* 1931, which proposes hybridization, a way of representing the atomic bonds that can explain the properties of chemical compounds.

In 1865 August Kekulé published an article in which he suggested for the first time what the structure for benzene really was, although it was the winner of the Nobel Prize in Chemistry, Linus Pauling (below), who found a way to represent its atomic configuration.

Watch Out! Explosive!

WHAT? Dynamite

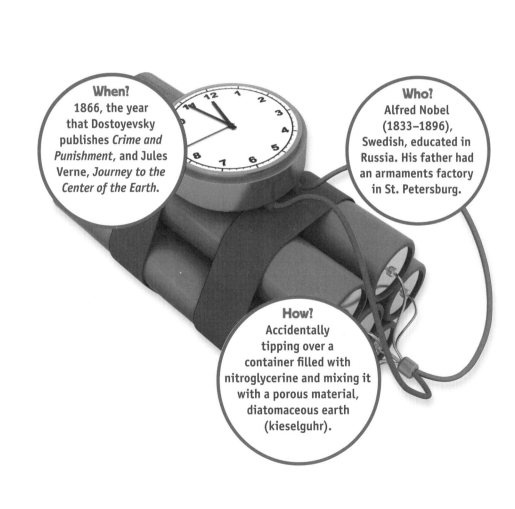

When?
1866, the year that Dostoyevsky publishes *Crime and Punishment*, and Jules Verne, *Journey to the Center of the Earth*.

Who?
Alfred Nobel (1833–1896), Swedish, educated in Russia. His father had an armaments factory in St. Petersburg.

How?
Accidentally tipping over a container filled with nitroglycerine and mixing it with a porous material, diatomaceous earth (kieselguhr).

My dynamite will sooner lead to peace than a thousand world conventions. As soon as men will find that in one instant, whole armies can be utterly destroyed, they surely will abide by golden peace.
Alfred Nobel

According to a Greek myth, the Titan Prometheus stole fire that Zeus was transporting in his chariot, and gave it to mankind. This infuriated Zeus, who came up with a devious plan for taking revenge on those poor mortals. He ordered the creation of a woman full of virtues, Pandora, who was brought to Epimetheus (brother of Prometheus) as a noble gift from the gods. Prometheus was suspicious of the gift, but his brother fell in love with her and married her. Pandora had come to Earth with a simple box (actually a jar) and had been warned by the gods not to open it under any circumstances. Zeus, however, had bestowed curiosity upon Pandora, so she ended up opening the box. Disease, madness, vice, poverty — all the evils polluting humanity were released for eternity. Zeus had accomplished his revenge.

On September 3, 1864, Alfred Nobel also opened his particular Pandora's box when he invented dynamite. Up until then, gunpowder was practically the only explosive that was used. Perfected by Schönbein and Hall, the product known as guncotton had caused serious accidents, and people were not confident about being able to control it. The same was true of another very powerful but terribly unstable explosive: nitroglycerine, created in 1846 by the Italian chemist Ascanio Sobrero. This "explosive glycerin" (as it was initially called by Sobrero) was dangerous, since a single shock, a jolt or direct sun-

Alfred Nobel was born in Stockholm in 1833 into a family of engineers. He was educated in Russia and worked in his father's armaments factory until it went bankrupt. When he returned to Sweden, he discovered a way to control the explosion of nitroglycerine, which made him a millionaire. He also invented other explosives and invested in oil wells in the Caucasus. Before he died, he bequeathed most of his fortune to the Nobel Foundation.

. . . .

It could have exploded at any moment, but Nobel observed that the earth on the floor had absorbed the nitroglycerine, and the mixture had formed solid, stable clumps that looked like frozen lava.

. . . .

St. Petersburg, the city where Alfred Nobel lived between 1839 and 1863, from the age of nine to thirty years old. At the time, St. Petersburg was the capital of Russia, and her "Window on Europe," founded by the Tsar Peter the Great in 1703 on the delta of the Neva River.

light was all it took to detonate it.

The instability of a nitric ether of glycerin needs to be controlled and that is what a Swedish chemist named Alfred Nobel undertook to investigate. The third of four brothers, Alfred was born in Stockholm on October 21, 1833, to a family with a long tradition as inventors. They soon immigrated to St. Petersburg (Russia) where his father (Immanuel Nobel), an expert on explosives, founded a torpedo factory, a shipyard and a munitions factory. Returning to Sweden, Alfred Nobel founded his own nitroglycerine factory in 1862. Patiently, and often recklessly, he experimented on nitroglycerine with a view to reduce the high sensitivity of the explosive that prevented use in its pure form. His investigations ended up completely destroying his lab, and cost the lives of five of his assistants, including his brother Emil.

One day, when entering the laboratory, he was terrified to see that he had accidentally spilled a large amount of nitroglycerine on the floor. It could have exploded at any moment, but Nobel observed that the earth on the floor had absorbed the nitroglycerine, and the mixture had formed solid, stable clumps that looked like frozen lava. The whitish earth that is used to transport containers of nitroglycerine had prevented friction. Known as diatomaceous earth, it turned out to be the solution to the puzzle. Nobel prepared various mixtures of nitroglycerine with the earth and finally found a way to control it so that it was no longer unstable. This solid, stable mass was what he had been searching for, and he had just accidentally invented dynamite (so named for the Greek word dynamis which means "strength").

The invention made him a multimillionaire. He founded several factories and introduced dynamite in the United States and Europe. Dynamite was immediately substituted for nitroglycerine in demolitions and mining. Its stability made it very safe to store, since a detonator was necessary to make it explode.

Not satisfied with his finding, Nobel spent the rest of his life working and researching in the field of explosives. In 1873, he created explosive gelatin, a mixture of nitroglycerine and nitrocellulose, more powerful than dynamite itself. And he did not stop there. In 1880, he obtained a patent for an automatic brake and an explosion proof boiler. In 1884, he also found a method for the continuous distillation of petroleum, which marked the start of the Russian oil industry, and further increased his immense personal fortune. His last contribution came in 1888, when he created ballistite, a mixture of nitroglycerine and nitrocellulose, from which he obtained a smokeless powder.

Nobel spent summers at his mansion in Stockholm, but in winter he retired to his villa in San Remo (Italy). He died there on December 30, 1896, at the age of 63. But his final contribution was yet to come. In his last will and testament, he had written his surprising and (extremely generous) final wish:

Grenade in the shape of a pineapple, designed by the British in 1916. It was called "Mk 2" and contained TNT but was soon replaced by a type of gunpowder that produced the proper amount of fragmentation.

I, the undersigned, Alfred Bernhard Nobel, do hereby, after mature deliberation, declare the following to be my last Will and Testament with respect to such prop-

Stockholm, birthplace of Alfred Nobel and where he returned at the age of 30 to continue his research.

erty as may be left by me at the time of my death. . .

The whole of my remaining realizable estate shall be dealt with in the following way: the capital, invested in safe securities by my executors, shall constitute a fund, the interest on which shall be annually distributed in the form of prizes to those who, during the preceding year, shall have conferred the greatest benefit to mankind. The said interest shall be divided into five equal parts, which shall be apportioned as follows: one part to the person who shall have made the most important discovery or invention within the field of physics; one part to the person who shall have made the most important chemical discovery or improvement; one part to the person who shall have made the most important discovery within the domain of physiology or medicine; one part to the person who shall have produced in the field of literature the most outstanding work in an ideal direction; and one part to the person who shall have done the most or the best work for fraternity between nations, for the abolition or reduction of standing armies and for the holding and promotion of peace congresses.

The prizes for physics and chemistry shall be awarded by the Swedish Academy of Sciences; that for physiological or medical work by the Caroline Institute in Stockholm; that for literature by the Academy in Stockholm, and that for champions of peace by a committee of five persons to be elected by the Norwegian Storting [Parliament]. It is my express wish that in awarding the prizes no consideration whatever shall be given to the nationality of the candidates, but that the most worthy shall receive the prize, whether he be a Scandinavian or not.

This Will and Testament is up to now the only one valid, and revokes all my previous testamentary dispositions, should any such exist after my death.

Paris, 27 November, 1895

Alfred Bernhard Nobel

Twenty days after his death, the document was opened, and, as Alfred Nobel had ordered, approximately 30 million Swedish Crowns were allocated to create the Nobel Foundation. Based in Stockholm, it is responsible for administering and staging the world-renowned Nobel awards ceremony that takes place every December 10.

The Sveriges Riksbank Prize in Economic Sciences was established in 1968 in Memory of Alfred Nobel, and first awarded in 1969 to the Norwegian Ragnar Frisch, and Jan Tinbergen from Holland. The first Nobel Prize in Physics went to W. C. Röntgen; the first in Chemistry, to Jacobus van 't Hoff; the first in Physiology and Medicine to Adolf von Behring; the first in Literature to Sully Prudhomme; and the first Peace Prize to Frédéric Passy.

Each winner is presented with a gold medal, a certificate and a sum of money that varies every year. In 2013, a prize of 8 million Swedish kronor (slightly under one million dollars) was awarded to each recipient.

The Sweetest Bread Ever

WHAT? Saccharine

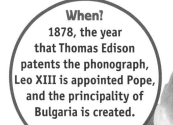

When?
1878, the year that Thomas Edison patents the phonograph, Leo XIII is appointed Pope, and the principality of Bulgaria is created.

Who?
Constantin Fahlberg (1850–1910) Russian chemist, nationalized U.S. citizen and later German.

How?
This chemist, a sugar specialist, discovered that the bread he had brought home was too sweet, and deduced that it had been contaminated with something he had in his clothes from work, where he was investigating the oxidation of sulfonamides. It was ortho-sulfonamide benzoic, i.e., saccharine.

Coal tar is a brown, viscous liquid that is often used as an anticorrosive and for waterproofing. This oil is flammable and smells of mothballs. Given such a description, you probably wouldn't use it to sweeten your coffee. But, strangely enough, saccharine and tar have a curious relationship.

The year was 1879. The chemist Ira Remsen was in the laboratory at Johns Hopkins University in Baltimore, where they were working with chemical reactions of viscous components. One member of the team was the German Constantin Fahlberg, who was temporarily helping Remsen investigate the oxidation of ortho-sulfonamides, components of the toluene hydrocarbon.

One evening after work, while having dinner at home, Fahlberg noticed that the bread had an extremely sweet taste. He had not washed his hands, and this seemed responsible for the change in taste. Back at the lab, he followed the trail of that component, until he managed to find that the sweet particle derived from tar. He had just discovered o-sulfamoylbenzoic, which he named "saccharine."

Bronze relief on the cenotaph of Constantin Fahlberg in a cemetery in the southern German city of Magdeburg. Fahlberg discovered the sweet taste of o-sulfamoylbenzoic in 1878, while analyzing the chemical components of coal tar.

The first artificial sweetener in history was between 100 and 300 times sweeter than sucrose from common sugar and had absolutely no calories.

Fahlberg patented the product in Europe and, with his uncle Adolph List, a Leipzig industrialist who immediately realized its commercial value, founded the firm Fahlberg, List & Co.

Manufacturers of sugar took saccharine as a serious threat to their business. Several critics soon appeared who claimed that the sweetener caused peptic, or digestive problems. In various countries restrictive laws were passed with regard to its production and consumption. It was the so-called "sweet war," with the big state sugar monopolies and saccharine manufacturers hurling around all sorts of accusations. In 1888 the *Journal des fabricants de sucre* reported:

Saccharin is a sweetener increasingly found in small packets on tables in cafes, as a substitute for sugar, which has more calories.

Saccharin is eliminated by the kidneys, when these organs are functioning well. But it cannot be completely eliminated from stomachs that are ill or fatigued. In this case, it forms deposits, and saccharin consumption must then be stopped immediately.

The extraordinary sweet taste of the bread led Fahlberg to suspect that it had been contaminated by a laboratory product.

The controversy reached the point that in 1908 the International Conference for the Repression of the Use of Saccharine was held in Brussels, which led to a ban on saccharin in most countries. But then came the First World War and, given the shortage of sugar, many governments ordered the use of saccharine.

The controversy over the toxicity or safety of saccharine was compounded by the discovery of a new no-calorie artificial sweetener, sodium cyclamate (E 952).

Discovered in 1937 by a student at the University of

Illinois (Michael Sveda), its use in the United States has been banned since 1970 by the Food and Drug Administration (FDA). A ban was also instituted on the use of saccharine in 1977, as it was considered to be carcinogenic, based on experiments with mice in Canada.

Saccharine and other artificial sweeteners can be safely consumed by diabetics. The pressure from this group finally resulted in a lifting of the ban on saccharine, and it was then considered safe in the United States. However, for several years it remained under suspicion, and was subjected to strict labeling rules with phrases like: "This product contains saccharine, which has been determined to cause cancer in laboratory animals." Finally, the National Institute of Health (NIH) removed saccharine from the list of carcinogens. In the European Union, it is authorized for consumption.

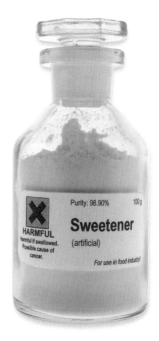

Bottle of artificial sweetener, a symbol of modern times.

Sweeteners and Palatants

Artificial sweeteners include saccharine, sodium cyclamate, aspartate and NHDC. They have no calories, and very small doses have a very intense effect. The problem is a disagreeable aftertaste. To avoid this, they are mixed with flavoring such as fruit, in order to attract human consumers. In the case of animals, it has been shown that if piglets are provided with sweetened food, their weight increases twice as fast than if they didn't have sweeteners. And they gain weight even faster if sweeteners have been added to enhance the flavor of milk

Accident in the Lab

WHAT? Polyethylene

When?
1898, the year the Spanish-American War breaks out over control of Cuba. Émile Zola publishes "J'Accuse" to protest the Dreyfus Affair.

Who?
Hans von Pechmann (1850–1902), a German chemist, professor in Munich and Tubingen, also established the symmetrical structure of anthraquinone.

How?
Accidentally heating diazomethane. When his colleagues studied the white, waxy substance he had created, they found that it had long chains of ethylene and named it "polyethylene."

. . . .

On account of its durability, good transparency, ease of processing and low cost, manufacture of polyethylene has reached 60 million tons per year.

. . . .

From supermarket bags and bottles of water or soda to dolls, polyethylene is the industrial plastic most widely used. It is found in a long list of everyday products. On account of its durability, good transparency, ease of processing and low cost, manufacture of polyethylene has reached 60 million tons per year, a figure that has become a serious problem for the environment, especially on account of it being tossed into the seas and oceans of our planet. Polyethylene is a non-biodegradable material but may be transformed by the action of sunlight (photodegradation) in a process that takes 150 years to complete. Therefore, it can be harmful, especially to marine life.

Low-density polyethylene, or LDPE, is the most widely used material in plasticulture for covering nurseries.

The history of this material, also known by the acronym PE, dates back to 1898, when the German chemist Hans von Pechmann discovered it by accident while heating diazomethane, an organic compound that he had discovered four years earlier. However, this whitish substance was not synthesized as we know it today until 1933, by Reginald Gibson and Eric Fawcett, while working for ICI Laboratories. They were experimenting with a mixture of ethylene and benzaldehyde when they produced a white, waxy material. It took two more years for another chemist, Michael Perrin, to develop this serendipity into a reproducible, high-pressure synthesis that would make polyethylene one of the bases of the chemical industry. The finding led to the industrial and commercial development of polyethylene by Imperial Chemical Industries, a company in Northwich, England.

This thermoplastic can be repeatedly softened by heat, and likewise, hardened by cooling. The first applications for it soon appeared. Because of its low permittivity (unaffected by electric fields) and water resistance, polyethylene was initially used as insulation in submarine cables and for coating other types of conductors, such as high frequency cables used in military installations. Later, its use in consumer products became widespread.

Types of polyethylene

Polyethylene is classified into several categories based on density, crystal structure and molecular weight. In the so-called UHMWPE, a type of thermoplastic polyethylene, the molecular weight can be several million, resulting in a very strong plastic, but inefficient for packaging or coverings that require some flexibility. The polyethylene used in greenhouses is low density, hence its poor resistance to type B ultraviolet rays, which are 5% of ultraviolet radiation and the most damaging. When exposed to this radiation, the carbon double bond, which is the matrix polymer, degrades and creates free radicals that end up destroying it.

The Flask That Wouldn't Shatter

WHAT? Safety Glass

When?
1903, the year the companies Harley Davidson and Ford are founded. George Orwell is born.

Who?
Édouard Benedictus (1878–1930), French chemist.

How?
In the laboratory he accidentally dropped a flask containing the remnants of cellulose nitrate. It was completely cracked, but the fragments did not scatter.

In the early twentieth century, when the American manufacturer Henry Ford set out to produce cars, he also developed a web of industries related to this emerging sector. The company's first car, the Ford Model T, appeared on the market on October 1, 1908. The steering wheel was on the left, the engine and transmission were hidden, and it offered 20 horsepower with a top speed of 45 miles per hour. All for the price of 825 dollars. The design of the car in question was quite spartan, and in those days, safety was not a primary concern. Only the windshield offered protection, but it was a laminate type that shattered into pieces on impact. By 1920, enclosed vehicles had started to become popular (then called indoor driving), but the windshield would shatter when struck.

Interestingly, safety glass had already been invented years before, but automakers did not see the value of introducing it in their cars. They believed that safety was not up to them but to the drivers.

The 1908 Ford Model T was the first vehicle to have safety glass. It was said that the car had many small glitches, but few big ones. 15 million were manufactured during the 19 years of production.

Credit for the discovery of this glass is due to the French chemist Édouard Benedictus. One morning in 1903, Benedictus was working in his laboratory when he climbed a ladder to reach some reagents. In so doing, he accidentally dropped a glass flask on the floor. To his surprise, he found that, despite the strong impact, the bottle was not broken, and the glass pieces held together in the shape of the container. The flask had contained a solution of cellulose nitrate that had since evaporated, leaving a thin, dry film of the substance in the container. He did not pay much attention to it.

But a few days later, Benedictus read an article in the newspaper about car accidents resulting from this new invention. According to the newspaper, most injuries were cuts resulting from shattered windshields. All of a sudden, the French chemist put two and two together.

To his surprise, he found that, despite the strong impact, the bottle was not broken and the glass remained more or less cohesive, preserving the shape of the container.

He returned to the laboratory and began experimenting with various coatings of cellulose nitrate applied to breakable glass. After a few days, he had made the first laminated safety glass, which was patented under the name "Triplex."

His invention did not get off to a good start. Car manufacturers considered it too expensive and initially did not back Benedictus's invention. In fact, the first large-scale application of the glass was for gas masks in the First World War. It was not until a few years later, when carmakers saw that the glass improved the performance of their models, that they began to include it in their assembly. The first safety windshield in history was incorporated into BMW's model DIXI 3-15, produced between 1928 and 1929.

Totaled car. Thanks to the use of a sheet of cellulose glass, the broken pieces have not shattered.

Let's Call It a Wrap

WHAT? Cellophane

Who?
Jacques Edwin Brandenberger (1872–1954), Swiss chemical and textile engineer, worked for a French company, which developed a mercerized cotton.

When?
1908, the year the Teatro Colón opens in Buenos Aires. General Motors is founded. Tunguska meteorite falls.

How?
A spilled glass of wine was the trigger. Brandenberger wanted to invent something that would prevent restaurant tablecloths from becoming too dirty. He sought an impermeable substance and tried to cover the tablecloths with cellulose, but this formed sheets that came off easily. The placemats were a failure but proved ideal as transparent wrapping.

• •

Jacques Brandenberger greatly resented having to eat on dirty tablecloths, no matter how good the restaurant was.

• •

Serendipity can show up at any moment. Sometimes it's in the course of experimentation, or towards the end of the investigation, but it can also appear early in the process. It can happen that a chance event inspires the idea you had been searching for.

And so it happened on a night in 1908 when the chemist and textile engineer Jacques Brandenberger was dining with his wife at a restaurant in Zurich. Suddenly, at a nearby table, a customer spilled his glass of wine onto the tablecloth. This has happened to all of us at some point, but this was an important mess. When the Swiss chemist returned home, he started to think about a possible solution to such domestic mishaps. He envisioned a kind of clear coating that would make any fabric waterproof. With this idea in mind, he began experimenting in his home laboratory. After staining an enormous amount of fabric, Brandenberger tested viscose. Created in 1884 by the French scientist Hilaire de Chardonnet, viscose is a viscous organic liquid obtained by mixing cellulose with other components such as sodium hydroxide and carbon disulfide. This substance (now also known as rayon) worked miracles, but not against stains. The combination did not serve for what Brandenberger was looking for, but he had discovered a tough, clear film that separated easily from fabric.

The result of the experiment was a brittle and highly rigid material, very different from what he had intended to find. Purely by serendipity, he had just discovered cellophane. This shiny, thin, transparent film had possibilities. Brandenberger patented the discovery with the

Cellophane is still used today to wrap candy, bouquets, boxes of chocolates and other gifts.

French name cellophane (combination of the words cello, "cellulose" and diaphane, "transparent"). The company La Cellophane SA (based in Bezons, France) began marketing the product in Europe. The first enterprise to use it in the United States was Whitman's candy company, which used it to wrap chocolates. Cellophane was imported from France until 1924, when the DuPont company in the United States received the exclusive patent for manufacturing and marketing cellophane in North and Central America. At DuPont, the researcher William Hale Church patented a process to prevent condensation on the cellophane, which opened the doors to its use for food.

The low permeability of cellophane (not only air, but also grease and bacteria) immediately attracted the attention of the food industry. Whitman's was the first to use it to wrap their products. Little by little, new applications for cellophane were being discovered: things like adhesive tape, rubber lamination, film for wrapping food and decorative containers.

The development of this material was cut short by the appearance of a new product that was cheaper to produce: plastic. But cellophane is making a comeback. It is based on regenerated cellulose, a cleaner, more sustainable product. It is biodegradable and, unlike plastic, does not derive from a non-renewable raw material (oil).

Bouquet of roses wrapped in cellophane. In addition to its protective role, its transparency allows you to enjoy the contents.

Just Fooling Around

WHAT? Nylon

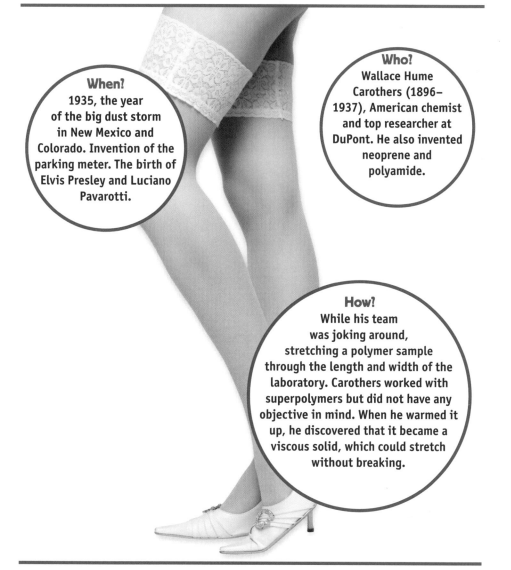

When?
1935, the year of the big dust storm in New Mexico and Colorado. Invention of the parking meter. The birth of Elvis Presley and Luciano Pavarotti.

Who?
Wallace Hume Carothers (1896–1937), American chemist and top researcher at DuPont. He also invented neoprene and polyamide.

How?
While his team was joking around, stretching a polymer sample through the length and width of the laboratory. Carothers worked with superpolymers but did not have any objective in mind. When he warmed it up, he discovered that it became a viscous solid, which could stretch without breaking.

There is no doubt that inspiration comes when one is working. And the American chemist, Wallace Hume Carothers knew a lot about this. After earning his doctorate in 1924 from the University of Illinois, he joined DuPont in Wilmington, Delaware, as the Research Director for organic chemistry. A specialist in polymerization, he soon achieved his first success. In 1931, Carothers created a revolutionary synthetic rubber, neoprene, which was derived from vinyl acetylene and in many ways superior to natural rubber. A tireless researcher into synthetic substitutes for natural fibers such as silk and cellulose, he also invented several polyesters. His career culminated in the finding that concerns us here.

Wallace's team was working on the composition of natural polymers, when they noticed a specimen that was highly elastic and had a silky appearance. No matter how much they stretched it, it never seemed to break. That's when they started playing with that ball of indestructible material. They stretched it and stretched it, forming a very long rope that reached almost to the lobby of the building. Surprised by the resiliency of the fiber, they began to focus their work in that area. They discovered that by polycondensation of substances, such as hexamethylenediamine and adipic acid, they were able to create a strong, elastic, artificial fiber. Nylon had just been invented. This fiber did not need to be ironed, was mothproof (damage from moths was widespread at that time), and its qualities made it a strong candidate as a substitute for silk and rayon.

The name "nylon" does not derive from a combination of "New York" and "London," as has often been said. Before it received its final name, many possibilities were considered: Duparooh, Wacara, Delawear, Dusilk, Moursheen, Rayamide, Silke and Norun. Finally the directors of DuPont opted for a combination of "nyl" (a syllable

In 1935, DuPont patented a new fiber called "nylon," called a miracle fiber because of its many properties. It was introduced to the world in 1938.

• •

No matter how much they stretched it, it never seemed to break. They had just discovered an indestructible fiber that was mothproof, elastic and very pliable.

• •

chosen at random) and "on," which in English is used as a suffix for various fibers. The patent for nylon filed by Carothers was granted in 1937. It was its first application that brought immediate fame to this synthetic fabric: nylon stockings. The following comes from DuPont's promotional literature:

> The object of this invention is the preparation of materials similar to silk-like materials, but superior in elasticity and wear resistance. This is achieved by preparing the knits from linear condensation polyamides.
>
> This preparation of woven materials usually results in increased elasticity as compared to those made by ordinary methods. Therefore, it is used in the manufacture of very tight garments and must be able to withstand tension without being permanently misshapen. Currently, the production of stockings is dominated by silk. It is the only known fibrous material with the requisite elastic properties. Eighty percent of the silk consumed in our country is used for this purpose. In the production of stockings, there have been several attempts to replace silk with artificial fibers, particularly a cellulosic type, but none have been successful. This type of stocking has a greater tendency to wrinkle in the knee and ankle than silk stockings, to increase in diameter and shorten in length. It also tends to slide over the skin to adjust to the leg movements. In short, it does not adhere well and is baggy in the knee area.

The invention of nylon allowed the production of many items at an affordable cost. Unfortunately, its inventor, Wallace Carothers, suffered from a serious manic-depressive disorder and committed suicide by taking cyanide in 1937, soon after his sister died and before the birth of his first child.

The round parachute was invented in the nineteenth century to protect travelers in hot air balloons from falls. Initially, they were made of silk, but during World War II, when most silk-producing areas were in the hands of the Japanese, the Allies invented nylon parachutes..

As a result, these stockings made with artificial fibers are worse than silk stockings, and they cannot command very high prices.

Linear condensation products of polyamides have been found by which are obtained woven fabrics and stockings originating in synthetic fibers equal to those made from silk. In fact, most of these fibers derived from polyamides and provide fabric that is superior to silk. Synthetic stockings adhere properly and do not form bags.

The first fiber produced from a one hundred percent synthetic polymer was immediately accepted. In 1939, DuPont began to produce and market the nylon from its factory in Seaford, Delaware. The first nylon stockings came on the market in 1940, and due to the successful sales (4 million pairs sold in the first days), DuPont opened five more manufacturing plants.

World War II did not stop the growth of nylon, rather increased its production with the manufacture of parachutes, sleeping bags and tents for soldiers.

Carothers was the first industrial chemist to be admitted as a member of the National Academy of Sciences. He died in 1937, two years after his great find, having committed suicide while suffering from a severe depression.

A Fortuitous Fissure

WHAT? Photosynthesis

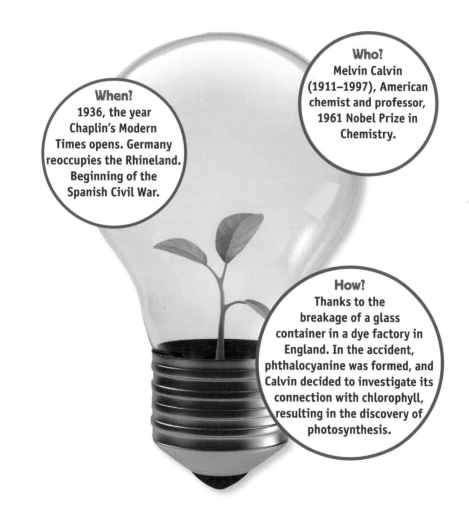

When?
1936, the year Chaplin's Modern Times opens. Germany reoccupies the Rhineland. Beginning of the Spanish Civil War.

Who?
Melvin Calvin (1911–1997), American chemist and professor, 1961 Nobel Prize in Chemistry.

How?
Thanks to the breakage of a glass container in a dye factory in England. In the accident, phthalocyanine was formed, and Calvin decided to investigate its connection with chlorophyll, resulting in the discovery of photosynthesis.

Photosynthesis is one of the most important biological processes on our planet. It is defined as a series of processes by which plants, algae and certain bacteria use energy from sunlight to convert inorganic matter in the environment (what is extracted from the soil, plus CO_2 from the atmosphere and the sun) into organic material. It uses the latter for its own growth and development. Photosynthesis is affected by five factors: light, water, carbon dioxide, pigments (chlorophyll) and temperature. It is known that the process is divided into two phases: photochemical phase, or Hill reaction, in which plants absorb light through pigments; and the phase of converting carbon dioxide, or Calvin cycle. It is this second phase that we are going to elaborate on, because it was discovered completely by chance.

The American chemist Melvin Calvin received his doctorate at the University of Minnesota in 1935, and a year later traveled to Europe to expand his research as a postgrad at the University of Manchester (UK), where the accident happened that would change the course of his academic and professional career. Imperial Chemical Industries (ICI) in Manchester, manufacturer of dyes, was producing a colorless compound called phthalonitrile. One day in 1936, the production manager noticed that one of the ingredients in the compound was displaying an unusual and intense bluish green color, apparently caused by a crack in the glass liner of the container. The substance was identified as phthalocyanine, the unique structure of which soon came to the attention of chemists.

Aristotle was the first to propose a relationship between sunlight and green plants, but this idea was forgotten until the seventeenth century when it was determined that air could be a source of food for plants.

- -

One day in 1936, the production manager noticed an ingredient in the compound was displaying an unusual and intense bluish green color.

- -

The team of Professor Michael Polanyi was working in the same city as Melvin Calvin. Right away, he realized that the structure of this substance created by Imperial Chemical Industries (ICI) appeared to be that of chlorophyll and a heme molecule. No one had yet managed to understand the activity and behavior of these molecules, and Calvin began experimenting with the new substance.

Upon returning to the United States, Calvin joined the chemistry department at the University of California, Berkeley. Inspired by the coincidence in Manchester, Calvin began his experiments in photosynthesis on cultivars of the unicellular green algae Chlorella pyrenoidosa.

In the early 1940s, two chemists, Martin Kamen and Sam Ruben, had just discovered so-called Carbon-14, used for the dating of organic specimens. However, Melvin Calvin used Carbon-14 for detecting the sequence in chemical reactions generated by plants when they transform carbon dioxide and water into oxygen and carbohydrates. It was about time that someone had finally figured out how to explain photosynthesis, the process of the absorption of carbon dioxide by plants. It was named the Calvin Cycle. The American chemist was awarded the 1961 Nobel Prize in Chemistry for this decisive contribution to the clarification of the process of photochemical absorption of CO_2 by the green parts of plants.

It took many years before Melvin Calvin, using carbon-14 as a tracer, discovered the sequence of chemical reactions that constitute photosynthesis, whereby plants transform CO_2 and water into oxygen and carbohydrates.

The Inert Material

Who?
Roy J. Plunkett (1910–1994), American chemist working at DuPont in New Jersey.

When?
1938, the year Franco arrives at the gates of Catalonia in Spain. Neville Chamberlain declares that he has secured "peace in our time." Nestlé founds the first factory for Nescafé. Superman is born.

How?
Researching the creation of new refrigerants at DuPont laboratories, he checked a tank of tetrafluoroethylene, and discovered that it had polymerized into Teflon, a nonstick, protective film.

. . . .

Inside the receptacle, the TFE had polymerized into a kind of white substance. Plunkett sensed that this was something new.

. . . .

Who hasn't been splattered by food at some point while cooking? This typical household accident can be avoided by means of a pan with a base made of Teflon. This word is familiar to most people, but few know that its discovery was the result of serendipity.

Roy J. Plunkett created this material, indispensable for kitchenware, in 1938. Having a doctorate in chemistry from Ohio State University, Plunkett was hired in 1936 by DuPont in New Jersey (where he was to remain throughout his entire career). At the time, company scientists were working on creating new refrigerants, specifically freons. It turns out that over time, these gaseous compounds of chlorofluorocarbons (CFCs) are very harmful to the ozone layer, and they were banned by the Montreal Protocol, but that's another story...

The point is that Plunkett was looking for ways to produce sufficient quantities of tetrafluoroethylene (TFE) for industrial use. To that end, he introduced TFE into refrigerated cylinders with solid CO_2 and submitted it to a vaporization process. One day, his assistant, Jack Rebok, was vaporizing the contents of one of these cylinders, and saw that something was wrong when he opened the valve. Inside the receptacle, the TFE had polymerized into a kind of white substance. Plunkett sensed that this was something new and began to analyze the greasy white powder. To his surprise, he saw it was inert to all solvents, acids and available bases. In other words, nothing reacted on contact with it, so it was not affected by heat or electricity, although it was extremely slippery. DuPont

Teflon is formed when the hydrogen atoms in polyethylene are exchanged with fluorine. It does not react with anything, it is an excellent electrical insulator, and it is also flexible, so it can be applied to any surface, such as a pan. However, even though its coefficient of friction is very low, if scratched with a metal object, it eventually flakes off.

The coefficient of friction of Teflon is so low that it is used to coat armor-piercing shells. However, it is used in rockets because of its ability to withstand a large range of temperatures, such as those that occur when a rocket enters the Earth's atmosphere.

took an interest in this substance, which was named polytetrafluoroethylene (PTFE) or Teflon, including it in its department of polymers.

Teflon was commercialized in 1946. Its applications were (and are) many:

- Coating for aircraft and spacecraft, due to its resistance to changes in temperature.
- In articulated industrial parts, due to its antifriction capability eliminating the need for lubricants
- Prosthesis (design of artificial organs and blood vessels) because it is flexible and nonstick. Moreover, Teflon does not react with other surrounding tissues
- Coating for cables due to its great insulating capacity and temperature resistance (able to withstand extreme temperatures from -270 to 300 degrees Celsius).
- In pots and pans, for its nonstick and low-friction capacity. In fact, it is the material with the lowest friction coefficient known.
- In structures subject to corrosion, as well as for tubing and cables for chemical products.

Currently, the Teflon® trademark is registered by E. I. du Pont de Nemours and Company.

Post It!

WHAT? Sticky Notes

BUSY at weekend?

Take mum to doctor's   Change shirt

Work late Thursday

Shopping wit...

VE[T]

Rew...

...th Ian

When?
1974, the year of the Carnation Revolution in Portugal. Watergate scandal. Juan Domingo Perón dies.

Who?
Spencer Silver (1941) and Arthur Fry (1931).

Diet club - ...et Cards!!

Monday

TAX!

Check

Friday SOK ✓

LUNCH now at 3.00PM

PASSPORT Phone

LUNCH with Sue...

How?
Spencer chanced to discover a removable adhesive. Years later, Arthur happened to remember this discovery while singing in church.

• •

He was tired of the bookmark in his book of psalms falling to the ground every few minutes, and it occurred to him that it would be ideal to produce one that was slightly adhesive.

• •

In the 1970s, the American company, Minnesota Mining & Manufacturing (better known as 3M) was looking for a new type of adhesive with a large bonding capacity. It was the chemical engineer Spencer Silver, working in the Corporate Research Laboratory, who finally came up with an unexpected product. It was an adhesive that was very easy to apply and peel off, but company executives didn't find a valid application for it at that time. After many trials, Silver's product fell into oblivion. Several years later, as chance would have it, another investigator from the same company, Arthur Fry, remembered the inven-

Did you know?

• Since being launched, Post-it notes have always been recyclable.
• The notes are available in eight standard sizes, 25 shapes and 62 colors.
• A study of more than 1,000 clerks in the United States, conducted in 1998 by the Gallup Organization and the Institute for the Future, concluded that each worker received eleven messages on Post-it notes daily.
• More than 500 million adhesive notes would be needed to surround Earth (considering that the circumference of Earth is 25,000 miles, and using notes that are 8 square inches).
• Dr. Spencer Silver, the 3M scientist responsible for discovering the adhesive used on Post-it notes, retired in 1996 with more than 22 U.S. patents to his name.

tion while singing in his church choir one morning in 1974. He was tired of the bookmark in his book of psalms falling to the ground every few minutes, and it occurred to him that it would be ideal to produce one that was slightly adhesive. Then he remembered Silver's light adhesive. It was not easy to convince the company, whose prestige was based on the manufacture of highly adhesive products. Finally, in 1977, the company's first Post-it prototypes were ready, and they decided to test them in their own office first. Internally, they proved to be a big success. The staff quickly depleted the stock and requested more sticky notes. It was also so popular among consumers that by 1979, 3M was selling its new sticky notes in eleven states in the American West. In 1981, 3M finally launched sticky notes to the whole world.

The rest is history. The canary yellow Post-it notes are present in offices and homes around the world, and its twentieth anniversary was celebrated in 2000 with more than 600 different products distributed in 100 countries. They have even been used to make works of art covering entire walls in the form of mosaics. They have also been adapted for use on computer screens, rather than posted to the side.

Brand names

Try it. In the office or at the store, do you ask for a sticky note or a Post-it? When you sneeze, do you need a tissue or a Kleenex? Indeed, neologisms are the order of the day, and often we do not even know how to refer to something specifically if we're not using the word in a generic sense. Here are the most common examples, mostly related to a particular trademark:

- Post-it (sticky note)
- Kleenex (tissue)
- Tupperware (lunchbox)
- Scotch tape (adhesive tape)
- Q-tip
- Zeppelin (dirigible)
- Diesel (gasoline)
- Aspirin (analgesic)
- White Out (correction fluid)

Put a Student on Your Team

WHAT? Conductive Polymers

When?
1977, the year of the first democratic elections in Spain in 42 years. First flight of the Concorde.

Who?
Hideki Shirakawa (1936), Japanese chemist, professor at University of Tsukuba, 2000 Nobel Prize in Chemistry, along with Alan G. MacDiarmid and Alan J. Heeger, for the discovery of conductive polymers.

How?
By making an error in the amount of reactive applied in the polymer oxidation process.

It does not take scientific genius to know that plastic is not a good conductor of electricity. Well, that was true until the arrival of conductive polymers in the late 1970s.

Plastics are polymers; that is, long strings of simple molecules repeated several times. The main components of these molecules are carbon and hydrogen atoms, in addition to other elements such as nitrogen, sulfur and oxygen. All of these are poor conductors of electricity. Therefore, polymers are often used as electrical insulators.

To get an idea of the different materials that are conductive and non-conductive of electricity, here is a simple list. Quartz, diamond, glass, silicon and germanium are non-conductive. On the other hand, metals, such as copper, iron and silver are conductive. Plastics and glass have a similar conductivity, which is almost imperceptible. Therefore, electrical conductors are usually insulated with polymeric plastic materials as protection from, for example, short circuits.

Image of the CES 2000 in Las Vegas. The Consumer Electronic Shows are fairs that present the latest in electronic technology, such as these extremely thin conductive polymer-based screens, made with OLED, an improved version of LED.

All this was well and good until a group of researchers managed to synthesize polymers (plastics) that are excellent conductors of electricity. These materials are so good that they are already considered as new synthetic metals.

The interest in finding a conductive polymer began in the 1960s. The aim was to revolutionize the industry by combining the low cost of the material, its flexibility, lightness and strength with a new capacity: conductivity. Researchers' efforts focused on oxidation as the most likely route to achieving this goal.

• •

The resulting polymer conducted electricity up to 10 million times more than a normal plastic! They had found the first conductive polymer in history.

• •

There was great excitement about who would be the first to obtain a really conductive polymer, but up until this point there had been little progress.

Among the scientific investigators was the Japanese chemist Hideki Shirakawa. In the mid-1970s, he was a researcher working in the chemistry laboratory of the Tokyo Institute of Technology. His experimental study was based on the conductive properties of acetylene when contaminated with other substances. This highly flammable gas was widely used in the chemical industry for processes of synthesis. During an experiment, a student on Shirakawa's team erroneously used a catalyst concentration that was 1,000 times higher than necessary for synthesizing the acetylene in polyacetylene. Of course, the result of the reagent was not as expected. To everyone's surprise, a polymer film formed that was metallic in appearance, but as flexible as aluminum foil. Shirakawa

Light is obtained by applying voltage to a thin film of conductive polymer. These are called OLED, organic light emitting diodes, and require only a low level of electrical stimulation to illuminate.

suspected right away that they had found something really interesting. After conducting several tests, he concluded that this new polymer, discovered by accident, had unusually elevated conductivity. The student's error with the catalyst had modified the polymer structure to the point of making it a new conductive material.

Two other scientists, Alan J. Heeger (University of

California) and Alan G. MacDiarmid (University of Pennsylvania), were also working on the conductivity of polymers when Shirakawa's finding came to their attention. The three decided to join forces to begin a new line of experimentation: modifying a polymer by oxidation with iodine vapor. We have already seen that scientists "contaminate" polymers with all kinds of substances and await a concrete response (in this case, electrical conductivity). Well, iodine was a success. The resulting polymer conducted electricity up to 10 million times more than a normal plastic! They had found the first conductive polymer in history. In 1977, their discovery was published in the joint article "Synthesis of electrically conducting organic polymers: halogen derivatives of polyacetylene, (CH)x," in the renowned *Journal of the Chemical Society*. The discovery and development of conductive polymers was awarded the 2000 Nobel Prize in Chemistry.

Currently, there are different types of conductive polymers and semiconductors, whose applications are widely varied: light-emitting diodes (LEDs), solar cells, light sensors, mobile screens, monitors, and all kinds of electronic components, among others. But there is still even more advanced technology on its way: OLEDs (organic LEDs). These require very little energy to emit light, and will be used for the extremely thin screens of the future.

Most organic polymers are insulators. To become conductive, they have been "doped," that is, provided with a coating that converts them into conductors. For this, they must be submerged in iodine vapor or an inert gas, such as argon, or bathed in an electrolyte solution.

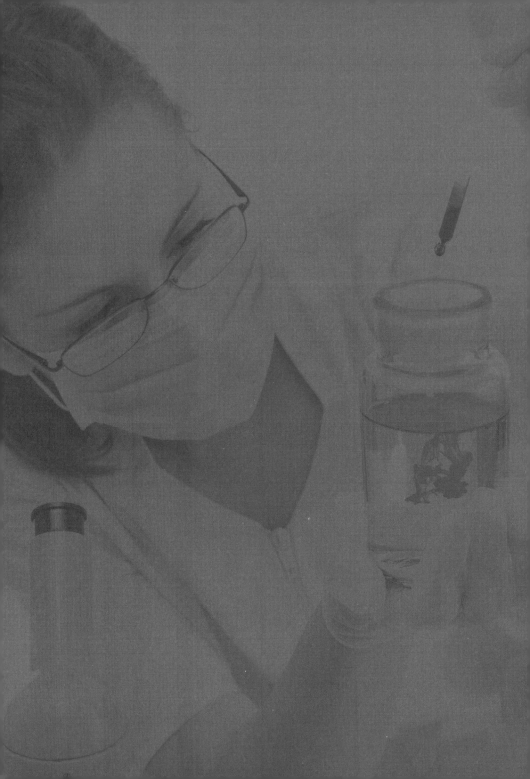

Great Historical Coincidences:

Biology,
Medicine,
Pharmacology

The Real Thing

WHAT? Coca-Cola

When?
1885, the year Mark Twain publishes *The Adventures of Huckleberry Finn* and the first publication of the Dow Jones Industrial Average.

Who?
John Pemberton (1831–1888), American pharmaceutical chemist. He obtained his degree at the young age of 19.

How?
A tonic against headaches and nausea sold in pharmacies would end up becoming the most famous soft drink in history.

The final formula for his medicinal tonic contained coca leaves and cola nuts and was mildly stimulating due to its caffeine content.

In the late nineteenth century, if you wanted to buy a Coke, you had to enter a pharmacy like the one run by John Pemberton, an American pharmacist, who went down in history as the inventor of the popular soft drink. In Jacob's Pharmacy (as the business was called), Pemberton sold all sorts of medicinal products with proprietary names, such as "Dr. Sandorf's Great Invigorator" and "Eureka Oil."

In 1885, the Atlanta pharmacist was working with various ingredients in order to create a remedy to relieve headaches and nausea. The final formula for his medicinal tonic contained coca leaves and cola nuts and was mildly stimulating due to its caffeine content. On May 8, 1886, Pemberton began selling the tonic in his Atlanta pharmacy. His accountant, Frank Robinson, branded it as Coca-Cola, thinking that the two letters "C" would stand out in advertisements published in the local press. Advertisements such as the one that appeared in the *Atlanta Journal*, referred to the drink as "Delicious, refreshing, stimulating and invigorating."

The drink was well received, and gradually the tonic began to be sold in other pharmacies and in bars where no alcohol was served (some of these counters being in the pharmacies themselves).

Before his death in 1888, Pemberton sold the trademark rights to pharmacist Asa Candler for $2,500. The tonic had become a refreshment much in demand, and sales increased dramatically between 1890 and 1900.

John Pemberton did not know how to take advantage of his invention. He sold the trademark rights to Coca-Cola to Asa Candler for $2,500. Thanks to a good promotional campaign, Coca-Cola became popular nationwide.

It was at this time that the Coca-Cola girls began to appear on posters and calendars to help boost sales, especially among the male customers.

Brands trying to imitate the soft drink began to appear. To distinguish it from the others, a competition was held in 1915 to create unique packaging, recognizable at a glance. Alexander Samuelson, of the Root Glass Company, gained recognition with the famous

Did you know?

• Coca-Cola is the most widely recognized brand in the world. 94 percent of the global population is familiar with it. It is sold in 200 countries, some that are not even officially recognized.

• On a normal day in the U.S., 66 million people drink Coke.

• Greta Garbo, Clark Gable, Buster Keaton, Judy Garland, Loretta Young, Carole Lombard, Spencer Tracy and Joan Crawford (who ironically would end up marrying the head of Pepsi-Cola) all appeared in ads for the soft drink.

• In 1931, the illustrator Haddon Sundblom drew the first ad showing Santa Claus drinking Coke, and in so doing created the image of Santa that is known today: a jolly fat man with a bushy white beard, dressed in red.

• Its most successful ad campaign debuted in 1970. It showed a group of children from around the world singing "It's the Real Thing" with the lyric "I'd like to teach the world to sing in perfect harmony." Performed by the New Seekers, it topped global charts.

• One of the first instances of cross promotion appeared in E.T. The Extraterrestrial when Elliot tells his alien friend, "Coke. You see, we drink it. It's a, it's a drink."

contoured bottle that almost 100 years later remains one of the most recognizable icons in the world. The designer was inspired by the fluted form of the berry of the kola nut, one of the original ingredients of the soft drinkHowever, there is a myth that it was actually inspired by the sinuous curves of the leading actress of the day: Mae West. Nothing could stop the drink's success, and it remains popular to this day.

The list of drinks that have imitated the popular soft drink is very long. Here are a few:

Afri-Kola, Café-Cola, Candy-Cola, Carbo-Cola, Celery-Cola, CocaBeta, Coke-Ola, Cola-Coke, Cold-Cola, Four-Cola, Cherry-Cola, Hayo-Cola, Jacob's-Cola, King-Cola, Koka-Nola, Koke, Kola-Kola, Loco-Kola, Mexico-la, Nerv-Ola, Nifti-Cola, PauPau-Cola, Penn-Cola, Pepsi-Cola, Prince-Cola, QuaKola, Rococola, Roxa-Cola, Sherry-Cola, Silver-Cola, Sola Cola, Star-Cola, Taka-Cola, Toka-Tona, True-Cola, Vani-Cola, Vine-Cola and Wine-Cola.

Nobody has been able to imitate the taste of Coca-Cola. Its secret formula, known by the code word Merchandise 7X, was guarded in the basement of the Trust Company Bank of Atlanta, Georgia, until 2011. In 1985, the company wanted to change the flavor, and this was a complete and utter failure.

A Gentleman in the Operating Room

WHAT? Surgical Gloves

When?
Tchaikovsky's *Sleeping Beauty* premieres. Discovery of the electron, births of Agatha Christie and Groucho Marx.

Who?
William Halsted (1852–1922), born in the U.S., spent his formative years in Europe and worked in many American hospitals.

How?
To protect the hands of his operating room assistant, who was suffering from dermatitis. It took several years to realize that wearing gloves protected not only doctors, but also patients from infections.

Already in the pre-Christian era, Hippocrates (460–377 B.C.E.) saw the importance of asepsis. We are referring to the set of scientific procedures used to protect your body from infectious germs, especially in surgery. The Greek physician recommended using wine or boiled water to wash wounds. Years later, Galen boiled the instruments used to treat the wounds of gladiators. However, it took a long time for medicine to pay due attention to this preventive measure.

Before getting to the story at hand, it is only fair to mention those who forged the path to making aseptic operating rooms universal. One of the main figures was the Hungarian physician Ignaz Philipp Semmelweis (1818–1865), who in 1847 established the etiology of puerperal fever. It seems that a colleague had died of blood poisoning after being infected when he pricked his finger while performing an autopsy. Semmelweis, who practiced at the Vienna General Hospital, realized that sepsis was prevalent in women whose births were attended by doctors and students from the autopsy room. To prevent this, he devised the first aseptic procedure, which involved washing hands and nails thoroughly with chlorinated water. In this way, Semmelweis managed to significantly reduce cases of sepsis.

The Hungarian physician Ignaz Semmelweis (1818–1865) was a pioneer in surgical asepsis. He recommended that obstetricians wash their hands with a disinfectant solution of chloride of lime before attending births, thus saving thousands of lives.

Years later, the chemist and microbiologist Louis Pasteur (1822–1895) established that the spread of germs could be stopped by heat. Another eminent scientist, the German Robert Koch (1843–1910), recommended the use of mercuric chloride as an antiseptic. Gradually, these practices began to be implemented in medicine. But many instances of infection continued to emerge from operating rooms. And this is where our protagonist enters the story.

• •

One winter morning in 1890, while operating, the surgeon noted that his assistant's hands showed an incipient dermatitis, likely caused by direct contact of the skin with antiseptics.

• •

William Stewart Halsted made numerous contributions to the field of medicine. He studied in Europe and worked in various hospitals. He investigated the use of cocaine as an anesthetic and systematized a number of major surgical procedures, but is best remembered for asking Goodyear to design gloves so that his assistant would be able to work in hygienic conditions in the operating room..

William Stewart Halsted was born into a wealthy New York family. After studying medicine at Yale University, he worked as an intern at Bellevue Hospital and New York Hospital until he moved to Europe to complete his studies. He stayed for two years in Vienna, Leipzig and Würzburg, where he met some of the leading medical figures of the period, such as the surgeon Theodor Billroth, the dermatologist Moritz Kaposi and the pathologist Hans Chiari.

Upon his return to the United States, he was appointed as the first head surgeon at the newly opened Johns Hopkins Hospital. This is where the coincidence unfolded that would lead to a major breakthrough in aseptic surgical applications. Carolina Hampton was Halsted's head nurse in the operating room. One winter morning in 1890, while operating, the surgeon noted that his assistant's hands showed an incipient dermatitis, likely caused by direct contact of the skin with antiseptics. With the specific purpose of protecting his nurse's hands, Halsted commissioned rubber gloves from Goodyear, the manufacturer of tires and rubber products. He wanted them to be thin enough to allow for precise manual work. For years, Halsted and his assistants wore these gloves as a protective measure. The wearing of gloves in operating rooms began in this casual manner.

That Cell Shouldn't Be There

WHAT? The Pap Test

Who?
George N. Papanicolaou (1883–1962), Greek physician and pioneer in the early detection of cancer, studied in Athens and earned his doctorate in Germany.

When?
1924, the year Howard Carter discovers the tomb of Tutankhamen. MGM is founded. Picasso paints his *Harlequin*. Thomas Mann writes *The Magic Mountain*.

How?
For a chromosome study with guinea pigs, while investigating the role of X and Y chromosomes, he isolated cancer cells and continued this line of research.

Cervical cancer is the second most common cancer among women. In fact, it accounts for 15 percent of all malignant tumors in women. However, cases of it have been decreasing due to early detection through cervical cytological methods. What is called the Pap test has proven to be the most effective means of detecting cellular abnormalities associated with this type of cancer.

This test, also called cervical cytology or Pap smear, was named after the Greek physician George N. Papanicolaou, and like many medical breakthroughs, came about through luck and a chance observation. Greek by birth, Papanicolaou's entire medical career developed in the United States, where he arrived, accompanied by his wife, in 1913. He began working in the Department of Pathology at New York Hospital and then joined the Department of Anatomy at Cornell University Medical College. Under the tutelage of Dr. Charles Stockard, he became involved in a series of experiments on the effects of alcohol vapor on guinea pigs and their offspring. These animals procreate continually, and the Greek physician requested a few for his own line of investigation. His research focused on a genetic study of chromosomes in order to determine the sex of the babies. For this research one needs eggs in

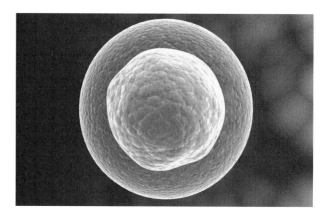

Papanicolaou's work consisted of finding cancer cells in vaginal fluid.

mitosis (before ovulation), and he was forced to sacrifice many female guinea pigs. That is until one day when he found a way to reduce the casualties in his laboratory. He thought that all female mammals must have periodic vaginal bleeding, however minor it might be. Therefore, he believed that these guinea pigs should also have it. To see if he was right, he began to take little vaginal smears from the guinea pigs with the help of a small nasal speculum. Upon placing the first samples under the microscope, he was amazed by the variety of cellular forms and cytological patterns. Encouraged by the results, he performed the first human vaginal cytology in history on his wife Maria.

Papanicolaou continued to perform cervical smears on women of various ages. In 1924, he chanced to perform cytology on a woman afflicted with cervical cancer and found cells that should not have been there: neoplastic cells. It then occurred to him that this test could be an excellent ally in early detection. That's when the Greek physician proposed the use of exfoliative cytology to diagnose cervical cancer.

The results of the smear tests performed by Papanicolaou at that time can be found in his article "The Sexual Cycle in the Human Female as Revealed by Vaginal Smears," published in the *American Journal of Anatomy* in 1933.

The scientific community was quick to acknowledge his discovery. Currently, the Pap test is still the most used and recommended for women for early diagnosis of cervical cancer.

Vaginal speculum used for examining the vaginal cavity. These speculums are also used for other cavities that should be kept open, such as the nose, eyes, ears and rectum. They were also used in former times by the Greeks, Romans and Arabs.

A Miraculous Fungus

WHAT? Penicillin

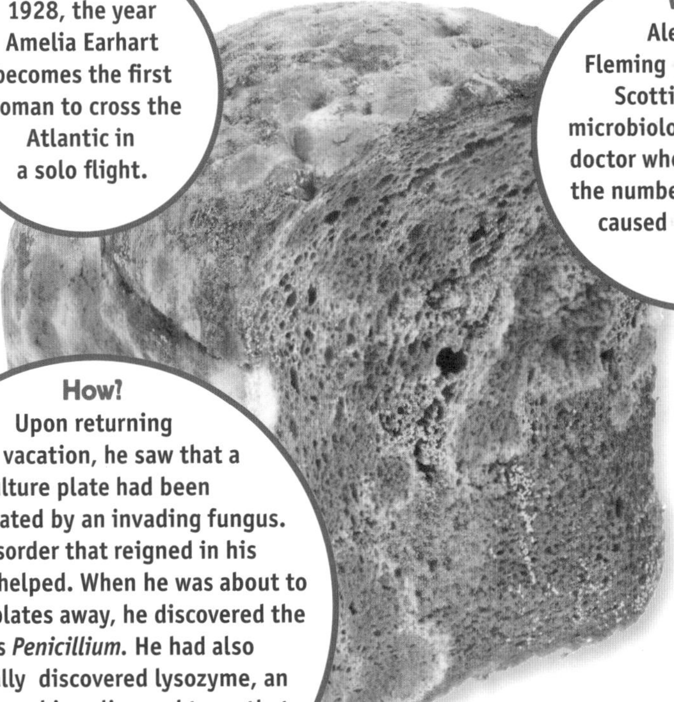

When?
1928, the year
Amelia Earhart
becomes the first
woman to cross the
Atlantic in
a solo flight.

Who?
Alexander
Fleming (1881–1955),
Scottish medical
microbiologist, a military
doctor who was struck by
the number of infections
caused by shrapnel.

How?
Upon returning
from vacation, he saw that a
culture plate had been
contaminated by an invading fungus.
The disorder that reigned in his
laboratory helped. When he was about to
throw the plates away, he discovered the
fungus *Penicillium*. He had also
accidentally discovered lysozyme, an
enzyme found in saliva and tears that
helps fight infection.

One of the greatest accidental medical discoveries in history is that of penicillin. In 1928, the bacteriologist Alexander Fleming was studying bacterial cultures (*Staphylococcus*) in the basement of St. Mary's Hospital in London. He was looking for ways to produce an antiseptic that would be more efficacious and resistant to infection. Fleming had been a military doctor on the front in France during the First World War, where he witnessed the high mortality rate of soldiers from infected wounds.

After a month of vacation, Fleming returned to his laboratory and found that the contents of a culture plate had been contaminated. It seems that summer temperatures had caused the uncontrolled development of an invasive fungus. Without paying too much attention, he tossed it onto a tray of disinfectant. Once more, fortune smiled upon Fleming, for the dish did not end up completely immersed in the liquid disinfectant. Not long afterwards, he received a visit from a former colleague. Explaining what he was working on, he went back to take a look at the contaminated culture plate and then indeed realized what was happening. Inside, the invading fungus was fending off bacteria, and destroying them.

This was important. He isolated the fungus right away, and cultivated it in another dish. He verified it as belonging to the genus *Penicillium* and named it *Penicillium notatum*. At first, scientists thought that penicillin would only be useful for treating minor infections and paid no further attention to it. But with the outbreak of the Second World War, the antibiotic became of interest to U.S. investigators who were attempting to emulate German military medicine, which made use of sulfonamides. Chemists Ernst Boris Chain

Statue of Alexander Fleming in Hastings Square, Darvel, Scotland. In 1909, at the age of 28, Fleming became a lecturer in bacteriology at London University. Prior to penicillin, he discovered lysozyme, an antibiotic enzyme, also by chance, when the product from a sneeze fell on a Petri dish containing bacterial cultures.

Fleming did not patent the invention of penicillin, which was a great service to humanity. At present, there are few drugs that are not patented because of the cost of research, which in Fleming's case and thanks to serendipity, was very low.

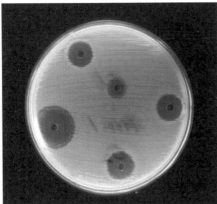

Staphylococcus aureus is a bacterium found on human skin but does not usually cause disease except in immune-compromised patients, usually hospitalized; under these circumstances, it can cause pneumonia.

and Howard Florey developed a purification method, which enabled penicillin to be synthesized and commercially distributed. Fleming did not patent his discovery because he believed this would facilitate the dissemination of an antibiotic necessary for the treatment of numerous infections that plagued the population. His discovery changed the history of medicine, opening the doors to a revolution in antibiotics.

Penicillin has been crucial to progress in specialized medical fields such as hematology and surgery, as well as giving a boost to intensive care units. The discovery of penicillin generated massive global research on antibiotic-producing microorganisms that continues to this day.

Alexander Fleming was knighted in 1944. A year later, he was awarded the Nobel Prize in Medicine along with the chemists Florey and Chain for their contributions to the development of penicillin.

A Hallucinatory Discovery

WHAT? LSD

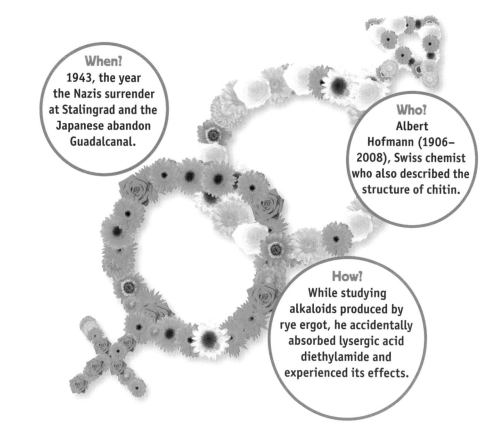

When?
1943, the year the Nazis surrender at Stalingrad and the Japanese abandon Guadalcanal.

Who?
Albert Hofmann (1906–2008), Swiss chemist who also described the structure of chitin.

How?
While studying alkaloids produced by rye ergot, he accidentally absorbed lysergic acid diethylamide and experienced its effects.

All of a sudden I was forced to interrupt my work in the lab-oratory in the middle of the afternoon and head home, find-ing myself affected by a remarkable restlessness, combined with some dizziness. At home I lay down and sank into a not unpleasant state of intoxication, characterized by an extremely stimulated imagination. In a sleep-like state, with eyes closed (I found the light of day uncomfortably bright), I perceived an uninterrupted stream of fantastic pictures, extraordinary shapes with intense kaleidoscopic displays. This condition continued for two hours, and then dissipat-ed.

> Albert Hofmann, discoverer of lysergic acid diethylamide (LSD)

LSD Molecule in 3D. This drug causes hallucinations even when eyes are open, distorts time perception, alters one's sense of self, and can cause synesthesia, a mixture of perceptions involving the senses in various ways, such as visualizing scents and colors when listening to music.

Having just received his doctorate in Zurich, the young Swiss Albert Hofmann immediately went to work in the chemical-pharmaceutical department of Sandoz Labora-tories (now Novartis), based in the city of Basel. A pre-cocious scientist, he was 23 when he embarked on a course of research aimed at finding medicinal applications for alkaloids contained in rye ergot. Ergot is a kind of para-sitic fungus that affects cereals, especially rye. When ac-cidentally consumed in bread, it can cause a disease called ergotism, which in the Middle Ages was popularly known as "St. Anthony's Fire," or "St. Anthony's Fever."

Soon after he began working in the laboratory, Hof-mann was able to synthesize lysergic acid diethylamide, the twenty-fifth lysergic acid derivative (hence its name, LSD-25). After several tests, he thought that given its similar structure to nikethamide (a known analeptic, that is, a central nervous system stimulant), this sub-stance could be used for stimulating the circulatory and respiratory systems. He experimented with diethylam-ide in animals but did not obtain the desired result, so he decided to abandon the research.

· ·

On April 16, 1943, Hofmann consumed 250 micrograms of LSD, thinking that this was the minimum dose.

· ·

Five years went by and in 1943, Hofmann returned to synthesizing LSD-25, driven, he said, by "a feeling that this substance may have other properties in addition to those established in the initial investigations." As chance would have it, during the process, some of the LSD solution was absorbed through his fingertips. He immediately began to feel strange and, as he subsequently noted in his diary, left work affected by "a remarkable restlessness, combined with some dizziness." On arriving home, he lay in bed and when he closed his eyes began to contemplate a series of "fantastic images, extraordinary pictures with intense kaleidoscopic color displays." The chemist thought these were the psychoactive effects of lysergic acid diethylamide, and three days later, on April 16, 1943, Hofmann consumed 250 micrograms of LSD thinking that this was the minimum dose.

He soon realized that he had just taken a powerful hallucinogenic drug. Right away, he began to notice that he was stammering and asked his assistant to accompany him home by bicycle. He later recounted that, during the trip, his vision was completely distorted and he had the sensation of being unable to move. He could barely stand, and everything around him was transformed into sinuous forms that scared him.

This is how Hofmann explained it in his book *LSD My Problem Child: Reflections on Sacred Drugs, Mysticism and Science:*

Albert Hofmann lived to be 102, having been the first person to try LSD, the psychedelic drug that he himself discovered.

Deliberate provocation of mystical experience, particularly by LSD and related hallucinogens, in contrast to spontaneous visionary experiences, entails dangers that must not be underestimated. Practitioners must take into account the peculiar effects of these substances, namely their ability to influence our consciousness, the innermost essence of our being. The history of LSD to date amply demonstrates the catastrophic consequences that can ensue when its profound effect is misjudged and the substance is mistaken for a pleasure drug. Special internal and external advance preparations are required; with them, an LSD experiment can become a meaningful experience. Wrong and inappropriate use has caused LSD to become my problem child. . . .

I had no inkling that the new substance would also come to be used beyond medical science, as an inebriant in the drug scene. Since my self-experiment had revealed LSD in its terrifying, demonic aspect, the last thing I could have expected was that this substance could ever find application as anything approaching a pleasure drug. . . .

In the LSD state the boundaries between the experiencing self and the outer world more or less disappear, depending on the depth of the inebriation. Feedback between receiver and sender takes place. A portion of the self overflows into the outer world, into objects, which begin to live, to have another, a deeper meaning. This can be perceived as a blessed, or as a demonic transformation imbued with terror, proceeding to a loss of the trusted ego. In an auspicious case, the new ego feels blissfully united with the objects of the outer world and consequently also with its fellow beings. This experience of deep oneness with the exterior world can even intensify to a feeling of the self being one with the universe. This condition of cosmic consciousness, which under favorable conditions can be evoked by LSD or by another hallucinogen from the group of Mexican sacred drugs, is analogous to spontaneous religious enlightenment, with the *unio mystica*. In both conditions, which often last only for a

The Hippy Movement was associated with LSD. Rejecting conventional culture, it was characterized by bold, flamboyant colors, flower-shaped emblems and

timeless moment, a reality is experienced that exposes a gleam of the transcendental reality, in which universe and self, sender and receiver, are one.

Finally, Hofmann fell asleep and woke up the next day without any feeling of discomfort or hangover. He had just discovered the psychedelic effects of lysergic acid diethylamide (LSD).

Years later its use was fairly common among psycho-analysts and psychotherapists, who used the substance in psycholytic therapy to break down the patient's psychological barriers. The actor Cary Grant's experience is well-known, since he publicly stated in 1961 that LSD therapy had changed his life: "It's a psychic energizer. . . . It releases the subconscious. It makes you see all your guilts, fears, repressions and insecurities. It makes you free."

Hippies are associated with the culture of love, music and LSD. Not all lived in communes, or took drugs for breakfast, but many did.

A year later, the U.S. Congress passed a new law on drugs and categorized LSD as an "experimental drug," prohibiting its clinical use. In 1966, Sandoz Laboratories suspended the sale of LSD. But its use was popular among young people, and the psychedelic experience of its consumption was associated with the hippie movement.

In 1968, the U.S. made possession of LSD for recreational use a crime. In 1970, the U.S. Congress passed what is now known as the Controlled Substances Act. (12 U.S.C. § 801.) Under that law, LSD is a "Schedule I" (most severely restricted) drug. Schedule I drugs are those that the government has deemed dangerous and without accepted medical use. (21 U.S.C. § 812.) As a Schedule I drug, possession, manufacture, and distribution of any amount of LSD for any purpose is illegal in the U.S. (21 USC § 802 (9).)

Please Pass the Salt

WHAT? Lithium as a Psychoactive Drug

Who?
John Cade (1912–1980), Australian psychiatrist. For three years, he was a prisoner of war in a Japanese prison camp, where he studied human behavior.

When?
1948, the year Gandhi is assassinated. The World Health Organization (WHO) is founded. The transistor and the first videogame are invented.

How?
Coincidentally using lithium salts in his experiments with guinea pigs. Lithium is used as a diluent of urea, but controlled experiments showed that used alone it was an effective sedative.

The year 1950 was especially fruitful in the field of psychopharmacology. Up until then, medicine had barely been able to treat serious psychiatric conditions effectively. Various methods had been attempted, such as Sackel's insulin comas, Von Meduna's convulsive cardiazol therapy, and Wagner-Jauregg's malaria therapy, but all without significant results. Psychological therapies were not very successful either, including psychoanalysis and the surgical procedures performed by Moniz, such as prefrontal leucotomies. So the arrival of psychotropic drugs was a positive development.

Interestingly, the discovery of several psychotropic drugs in this period was the fruit of both coincidence and fortuitous clinical observation. One example took place in 1948, when John Frederick Joseph Cade discovered the application of lithium as an effective psychoactive treatment. At that time, Cade was medical superintendent and psychiatrist at the Repatriation Mental Hospital in Bundoora, Australia. It had been found that patients with endocrine thyroid disease exhibited symptoms very similar to a manic-depressive disorder. Consequently, the Australian psychiatrist thought that this disorder originated from hormonal dysfunction and began extensive testing on animals. First he collected urine samples from both manic patients and healthy subjects. He then injected it into guinea pigs, causing some of them to suffer convulsions, prolonged unconsciousness, or even death. This confirmed his conjecture that the urine of these patients contained a toxic substance, first suspected of being urea and later on uric acid. It was then that he began to work with both substances, but because of their poor

John Cade experimented with guinea pigs, injecting them with the urine of manic-depressive patients. Some suffered convulsions, which led him to believe it was a hormone problem. Later, he discovered that by injecting them with lithium urate, the seizures ceased.

solubility, Cade turned to lithium urate, a very soluble salt. The psychiatrist then found that an injection of this saturated salt solution with 8 percent urea surprisingly prevented the seizures in guinea pigs that had been observed previously. Two hours after the injection, the animals experienced a lethargic state that disappeared within another two hours.

That put Cade on the definitive track of lithium carbonate, and he went from guinea pigs to humans. He began administering 1,200 mg of lithium citrate, three times a day, to a 51-year-old male who had been affected by manic episodes for five years. After one week, the patient's improvement was evident. After four months of treatment, the patient was able to return to his job. Cade continued to experiment with other patients and obtained positive results in all cases. In 1949, he published the results of his research in an article entitled "Lithium Salts in the Treatment of Psychotic Excitement" in *The Medical Journal of Australia*. It was the birth of psychiatric pharmacology.

The history of the first antidepressant drugs also contains an element of serendipity. Interestingly, their origin lies in the anti-tuberculosis drugs that had been used since the early 1950s. At that time, researchers Herbert Hyman Fox (Hoffmann-La Roche Laboratories in New Jersey) and Harry L. Yale (the Squibb Institute for Medical Research, Princeton, New Jersey) separately discovered a powerful anti-tubercular agent: isoniazid. Use of the drug reduced tuberculosis deaths from 188 out of every 100,000 U.S.

On numerous occasions, remedies are discovered by chance, but only after many hours of work in the laboratory.

Guinea pigs have performed great service to humanity as victims of all kinds of laboratory experiments. In Peru, where they originate, they are all *quwi,* a Quechuan word.

patients in 1904 to a mere 4 out of 100,000 in 1952: positive proof of its efficacy. Coincidentally, they found that this substance slightly stimulated the patients' central nervous systems, which was seen as a mild side effect.

In 1952, researchers Irving Selikoff, Edward Robitzek and George Ornstein, of the Sea View Hospital in Staten Island, found that a derivative of isoniazid, iproniazid, was more potent in stimulating the nervous system: patients exhibited much more vitality and increased social activity. Five years later, the first figures on the stimulating effects of iproniazid for treating depression were revealed at a meeting of the American Psychiatric Association (APA) in Syracuse, New York. A year after the meeting in Syracuse, iproniazid began to be marketed as a treatment for tuberculosis, although thousands of patients with depression also used it to treat their condition.

The fight against depression motivates the pharmaceutical industry because it affects an increasingly large number of people in developed countries. Women suffer almost twice as many cases of depression as men and are the main consumers of antidepressants.

The first drug specifically marketed as an anxiolytic (anti-anxiety medication) also had a coincidental origin. During the Second World War, penicillin was shown to be ineffective for treating war wound infections caused by gram-negative bacteria. Therefore, the antibiotic was administered mixed with phenoxyethanol, an antiseptic with antimicrobial properties, but this compound had a limited effect. So William Bradley, a

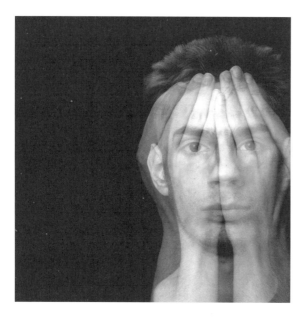

Anti-anxiety drugs are depressants of nervous activity. They are prescribed for anxiety and induce sleep but can be addictive if taken for too long or in high doses.

chemist from British Drug Houses Ltd. in London, tried to synthesize various analogues of phenoxyethanol with the aim of finding a more potent antimicrobial compound.

A member of his team, the Czech pharmacologist Frank M. Berger, noted that these compounds caused a reversible flaccid paralysis of the muscles in the animals tested. This led Berger to divert his aim from the initial experiment. Of all the compounds tested, there was one in particular, mephenesin, whose anxiolytic properties attracted the interest of anesthesiologists as an alternative to tubocurarine. But its effect was not very long in duration, so Berger and the chemist B. J. Ludwig began a new line of research in 1949. That led to the discovery of meprobamate, the first drug especially marketed as an anxiolytic, a muscle relaxant, an anticonvulsant and a tranquilizer.

The Australian Antigen

WHAT? The Hepatitis B Antigen

Who?
Baruch S. Blumberg (1925–2011), American scientist, specialist in infectious diseases, virology, genetics and anthropology.

When?
1963, the year the "red phone" is connected between the White House and the Kremlin, and Russia sends the first woman into space.

How?
Coincidentally discovering a reaction between blood samples from a New Yorker and an Australian aborigine.

To understand the background of this disease, let's go back in time and recount the curious chance discovery of the Hepatitis B virus (HBV).

Prior to the Second World War, it was still unknown that hepatitis was caused by a virus. It was suspected to be contagious because epidemics of this disease occurred frequently in unsanitary conditions and crowded public places. But finding out how it spread remained a complete mystery.

This changed in 1940 when F. O. MacCallum, a doctor specializing in liver diseases, proposed that hepatitis could be caused by a virus carried in human blood. How did he come to this conclusion? As so often happens in the history of medicine, he followed a path that led him to a most unexpected place.

MacCallum was responsible for the production of a yellow fever vaccine, a disease that was decimating soldiers on the African continent. Many men developed hepatitis a few months after receiving the vaccine. Since the vaccine contained human blood, MacCallum began to suspect that a contagious virus was contained in the serum. After several observations, his hypothesis grew stronger, and it was also revealed that hepatitis could be transmitted by means other than blood. As a result of these findings, the term "Hepatitis A" was coined to designate the infectious type, and "Hepatitis B" for that caused by homologous sera (Serum Hepatitis).

In the years that followed, many researchers tried unsuccessfully to find the infectious agents that caused these two types of hepatitis. Their investigations had reached a disappointing impasse when chance burst onto the scene.

In the late 1950s, the American scientist Baruch Samuel Blumberg was researching genetic variations in

There are seven types of hepatitis, and all are caused by viruses. Five of them live in blood, and the other two can be found in sewage.

. . . .

Experiments conducted in 1963 revealed that the blood of a hemophiliac from New York reacted with the serum of an Australian aborigine.

. . . .

the blood of different ethnic populations in order to explain why some people were more likely to get sick than others, and if this was hereditary. For this study, Blumberg had obtained blood samples from populations around the world.

By the 1960s, the American doctor had begun collaborating with biochemist Anthony Allison on a project to identify new blood proteins quickly and easily. They thought that the blood of a patient who had received multiple transfusions produced its own antibodies or antigens to immunize against foreign proteins. To test this, they used a technique called agar gel diffusion. Using blood samples that Blumberg had collected from all over the world, they analyzed possible reactions from the blood of patients who had received multiple transfusions.

After months of experiments, in 1963 they discovered that the blood of a New York hemophilia patient reacted with the serum of an Australian aborigine. They had already seen other reactions, but this was different: the Australian serum had only reacted with the serum of one of the twenty-four hemophilia patients in the comparison. What did it mean? It seemed they were dealing with a unique, foreign antigen, and this was causing the reaction. Intrigued, the researchers

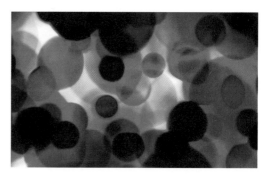

Hepatitis B is an infectious liver disease caused by a virus. Its presence may result in cirrhosis of the liver, liver cancer or liver failure. It is one of the most common infections, with 360 million people infected worldwide.

Uluru (Ayers Rock), the mountain sacred to indigenous Australians. The hepatitis B antigen is found within the indigenous population.

The antigen HBsAg of hepatitis B, viewed through an electron microscope. It is important to detect hepatitis early, before symptoms appear.

conducted analyses of the sera of hemophiliac patients and thousands of other blood samples. They then discovered that only one in 1,000 blood samples from healthy patients and hemophiliacs had not reacted with the hemophiliac's serum, while one in ten blood samples from leukemia patients did react.

They were closing in on the mysterious antigen rarely found in healthy patients, but frequently seen in patients with hemophilia and leukemia. At that point, they concluded that an unknown antigen in the blood of an Australian aboriginal reacted to antibodies from the blood of certain hemophilia and leukemia patients. It was highly likely that an infectious agent, a virus, was the explanation for the link between the Australian antigen and leukemia.

To clarify this link, they began to search for the Australian antigen in the blood of children with Down's syndrome, as they are especially susceptible to leukemia. They found that nearly a third carried the mysterious antigen. In 1966, in analyzing the blood of a boy with this syndrome, they found the final clue. In the first analysis, they found no trace of the antigen, but in the second trial they did. What had changed? Between the two trials, the little boy had contracted hepatitis. It was this coincidence that immediately led investigators to associate the two. After several tests, they found that the Australian antigen appeared far more often in patients with hepatitis. This became conclusive when one of Blumberg's assistants started feeling sick. After conducting tests for the Australian antigen, they indeed tested positive, and he soon developed hepatitis.

There were subsequent investigations by other teams, and at the end of 1970, all reached the same conclusion: the Australian antigen formed part of the virus that causes hepatitis B. They had just discovered the hepatitis B antigen, called the surface antigen of the hepatitis B virus, known by the acronym HBsAg, and also as the Australian antigen. That made an immediate clinical impact and contributed to the development of a vaccine for prevention of the disease, since the antigen consists of a glycoprotein that is inserted into the surface of the hepatitis virus, and when detected in the bloodstream indicates infection.

Acacia Xanthophloea, known in English as the fever tree, because of the belief that it grows in areas where malaria occurs. In Spanish, it is known as the yellow bark tree.

Bacteria Do Not Take Holidays

WHAT? The Bacteria of Stomach Ulcers

When?
1982, the year Felipe Gonzalez is named president of Spain. Groundbreaking ceremony for the Vietnam Veterans Memorial takes place in Washington, D.C. The first computer for popular use is put on sale. Premieres of *E.T., Blade Runner* and *First Blood*.

Who?
Barry J. Marshall (1951) and John Robin Warren (1937), 2005 Nobel Prize in Physiology or Medicine for showing that *Helicobacter pylori* is responsible for most stomach ulcers.

How?
Forgetting a culture in the laboratory during the Easter holidays. Until then, it was believed that bacteria could not live in a person's stomach, due to stomach acid.

Sometimes the human body suffers from colonization by certain persistent bacteria, capable of surviving in very harsh environments. This is the case of so-called *Helico-bacter pylori*, spiral-shaped bacteria that live exclusive-ly in the human stomach. The extreme acidity present in this organ made the scientific community reluctant to accept its chance discovery by an Australian doctor, Barry J. Marshall.

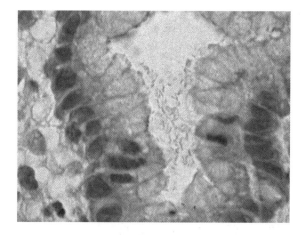

The history of this medical discovery began in 1979 when Dr. John Robin Warren, a doc-tor at Royal Perth Hospital, was investigating the presence of bacteria in the gastric mu-cosa of some patients. Barry J. Marshall was a young resident on the team who was charged with investigating these gas-tric bacteria. Marshall sought the help of Dr. C. Stewart Goodwin, a microbiologist at the hospital laboratory, to follow up on his research. Af-ter analyzing the bacteria, Goodwin concluded that it was bacteria of the species *Campylobacter* (initially named *Campylobacter pyloridis*). That said, Marshall be-gan the study by inoculating samples and incubating them for 48 hours at 95 degrees F. The results were neg-ative. There was no trace of the curved rods that had been observed in gastric biopsies. He made several at-tempts, but the results were always identical. There was no progress until serendipity arrived in the form of... Easter holidays.

Marshall took a break for five days and forgot to re-move the inoculated samples from the incubator. Upon returning, he went to check the plates and saw that

Helicobacter pylori, the bacteria infecting the gastric epithelium, causing stomach ulcers and gastritis. The name pylori (gatekeeper) derives from pylorus, the opening of the stomach that leads to the intestine.

· ·

Marshall took a break for five days and forgot to remove the inoculated samples from the incubator. Upon returning, he went to check the plates and saw that something had changed.

· ·

something had changed. In all of the samples, there appeared small colonies of bacteria, which he had attempted to cultivate many times without success. What had happened? On account of his forgetfulness, he had allowed the bacteria five days to grow, whereas previously he had only waited for forty-eight hours. This happenstance set him on the right track. He began to analyze these slow-growing microscopic specimens (0.04 inches) which had spiral forms that enabled them to withstand the extreme acidity of the stomach and develop into colonies of persistent bacilli.

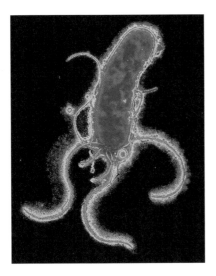

At that time, the medical community maintained that stress or excessive overeating were the causes of stomach ulcers and gastritis.

Following the discovery, Warren and Marshall confirmed that colonization of the stomach by this bacillus could be the real cause. However, initially, this hypothesis was not accepted, because it was thought to be impossible for any living organism to subsist in such acidic conditions. Attempting to confirm their finding, Marshall prepared a culture of *Helicobacter pylori* and simply ingested it. Within a week, the doctor developed all the symptoms of gastritis, and a biopsy revealed that he was infected with the bacteria. This was conclusive, and in 1983 he pub-

Isolated *Helicobacter pylori*. It was a struggle to convince the medical community that this bacterium was the cause of stomach ulcers.

lished his findings in an article entitled "Unidentified Curved Bacilli on Gastric Epithelium in Active Chronic Gastritis" in the medical journal, *The Lancet*.

Prior to this discovery, stomach ulcers were treated with drugs that neutralized acidity. In this course of treatment, ulcers often reappeared after the medication was stopped. Marshall and Warren discovered that antibiotics were effective in eradicating *Helicobacter pylori* colonies. A widespread bacillus, it is estimated that more than two thirds of the world population are infected. If not treated with antibiotics, the infection can persist for a lifetime, because the immune system is unable to eradicate it.

In 1994, Marshall founded The Helicobacter Foundation, and a year later his work was recognized with the prestigious Albert Lasker Award. This was the prelude to the 2005 Nobel Prize in Physiology or Medicine, awarded to both him and Dr. John Robin Warren, for the discovery of *Helicobacter pylori*.

Actually, this bacterium had already been discovered in 1899 by Walery Jaworski, a professor at Jagiellonian University in Kraków, while investigating sediments from human gastric lavage. He was the first to suggest that the bacteria he discovered could have some connection with gastric diseases, but as he wrote the article in Polish, it was largely overlooked. Before this, in 1875, some German scientists had discovered spiral bacteria in the human stomach, but they could not cultivate it, and the idea was soon forgotten.

Robin Warren, discoverer of *Helicobacter* bacterium, and creator of the urea breath test for detection. The breath emission of carbon dioxide with the isotope carbon-14 indicates the presence of urease in the stomach, indicating that there is an ulcer.

We Are Unique

WHAT? Genetic Fingerprints

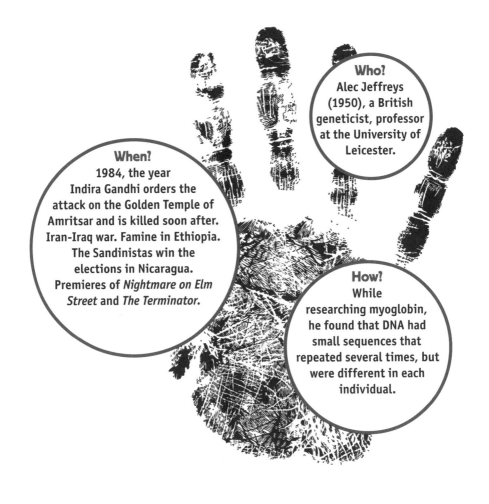

Who?
Alec Jeffreys (1950), a British geneticist, professor at the University of Leicester.

When?
1984, the year Indira Gandhi orders the attack on the Golden Temple of Amritsar and is killed soon after. Iran-Iraq war. Famine in Ethiopia. The Sandinistas win the elections in Nicaragua. Premieres of *Nightmare on Elm Street* and *The Terminator*.

How?
While researching myoglobin, he found that DNA had small sequences that repeated several times, but were different in each individual.

Within seconds it was obvious that we had stumbled upon a DNA-based method not only for biological identification, but also for sorting out family relationships. It really was an extraordinary moment.

Sir Alec Jeffreys

Use of DNA fingerprinting in the investigation of crimes has become commonplace. Thousands of people around the world also use this technique to determine paternity. There are huge databases that store the genetic information for millions of criminals and crime scenes. This so-called genetic fingerprinting, discovered by chance in 1984, has revolutionized fields such as criminology and forensic medicine, is used in the identification of human remains, in paternity tests, for compatibility in organ donations, in studies of wildlife populations, to trace origins and in the composition of food, among others.

The Croatian Juan Vucetich invented the process of fingerprinting to identify people. The invention was patented and developed in Argentina, where Vucetich was to obtain nationality. It was there that he first used it to solve a crime.

But how was it arrived at? One morning in September 1984, Dr. Alec Jeffreys was in his laboratory at the University of Leicester (UK). He and his team were investigating the gene for a protein called myoglobin and the molecular differences between distinct individuals. While observing a sample, they chanced to discover that there were regions of the genome that consisted of small DNA sequences that were repeated several times. The number of repetitions varied according to each individual analyzed, a somewhat perplexing barcode that was unique in each case.

Surprised by the discovery, Jeffreys obtained genetic samples from his technician, Jenny Foxon and compared them with those of her parents. Although it was somewhat blurry, it was relatively easy to detect that

• •

Genetic fingerprinting has revolutionized many fields, such as forensic medicine, where it is used to identify human remains. It is also often used in paternity tests.

• •

Every person's DNA is unique, and constitutes what is called genetic fingerprinting. It is used in forensics to find those responsible for a crime, and also to identify paternity. In forensic medicine DNA is sampled in blood, skin, saliva and semen.

the DNA coding (which would later be termed "genetic fingerprinting") was a combination of her mother's and father's, yet at the same time unique. Seeing this, Jeffreys quickly realized that he had stumbled upon a whole new method of identification based on DNA.

A few hours later, Jeffrey and his research colleague Victoria Wilson drew up a list of basic applications in which the newly discovered test could be used: such as paternity tests, DNA identification at crime scenes, identification of twins and matters related to immigration.

Eight months after the discovery of DNA fingerprinting, the test was applied for the first time in the case of a child who was being threatened with deportation. His kinship was proved, and he was allowed to remain in the UK with his family. Soon thereafter, it was used to solve the first case of paternity and, in 1986, used for the first time to determine the innocence of a young man accused of rape. In fact, the DNA test served to identify the real culprit.

Other milestones in DNA testing include identifying the body of the Nazi war criminal Josef Mengele, the authentication of the first clone in history (the famous sheep Dolly) and for investigating the impact of the Chernobyl nuclear accident on the DNA of subsequent generations.

In 1986, DNA testing evolved when biochemist Kary Mullis created a DNA amplification technique called the polymerase chain reaction (PCR). It allowed for genetic analysis from very small samples. This is now used to create international databases that record the DNA of convicted criminals. For his invention, Mullis received the 1993 Nobel Prize in Chemistry.

Is this child mine?

Higly accurate paternity testing became available in the 1980s. Increases in divorce, immigration and instances of infidelity have caused a rise in this type of testing. The procedure is very simple. First, one orders a sample collection kit online or by phone (of course, most people would prefer to conduct the whole process with the utmost discretion).

To obtain the DNA, all one has to do is gently rub the buccal mucosa of both the child and the parent with a cotton swab, and collect a sample of saliva from both. The test can also be performed directly at an accredited center, which avoids the risk of contaminated results. Kits are being sold on the internet for under $100.00.

From the Pharmacy to the Barber

WHAT? New Application for Vasodilator Minoxidil

Who?
The Upjohn Company, founded in 1886 in Kalamazoo, Michigan, U.S.A. Currently owned by Pfizer.

When?
1988, the year Perestroika begins in Russia. End of the Cold War.

How?
Upon receiving letters and phone calls from patients who exhibited unusual hair growth as a side effect.

Baldness is a condition from which men especially suffer. In fact, almost half of the adult male population between the ages of 20 and 64 suffers from hair loss problems. Alopecia can occur for the following reasons:

- Hormonal problems. Hair loss caused by issues such as elevated levels of male hormones (especially testosterone), abnormal thyroid and menopause
- Psychological distress. Such as anxiety, stress or depression
- Side effects. After undergoing radiotherapy, for example
- Infections and prolonged feverish states
- Dietary problems. For example, anorexia, vitamin deficiencies or anemia.

Minoxidil was first used as a vasodilator to treat high blood pressure. Just by chance, a secondary effect helps to prevent hair loss and stimulate its growth, and is most effective in young men and on the crown area of the head. A lower dose is used for women.

Not all types of alopecia are the same. There are several types:

- Androgenic alopecia. This is the most common type and mainly affects the male population. It is characterized by a receding hairline and/or hair loss on the top of the head, and above all at the back of the head.
- Scarring alopecia. Caused by a skin disorder such as inflammation, scarring, infection or burns. The scalp is damaged and follicles are destroyed, resulting in irreversible hair loss.
- Alopecia areata. This occurs as a symptom of a physical disorder or disease. It develops as a round or oval spot in one or more areas of the scalp.
- Diffuse alopecia. This mainly affects the female population. It is an overall thinning of the hair.

There are hundreds of remedies for combatting baldness. The most effective treatment, Minoxidil, endorsed

• •

It seemed that the Minoxidil they had been taking had an unexpected and very obvious side effect: accelerated hair growth.

• •

There are many remedies for hair loss, but few are effective. Traditional medicine puts most of the blame on stress or anxiety, but it is reasonable to believe that the cause is genetic, as in the case of someone whose hair turns white at the age of 40.

by the medical community, is a potent vasodilator whose efficacy in fighting hair loss was discovered by chance.

In the late 1980s, the Upjohn Company, based in Michigan, began receiving letters and calls from patients who had been using one of their antihypertensive medications for a while. It seemed that the Minoxidil they had been taking had an unexpected and very noticeable side effect: accelerated hair growth. This caught the company's attention, and after various tests, they began to produce a solution that was two percent Minoxidil as a treatment for baldness and hair loss. Years later, they developed a second solution, this time with five percent Minoxidil (best indicated for male baldness). These two lotions are currently the most commonly used products for combating baldness. Their effectiveness varies between twenty and fifty percent, depending on the concentration of the substance. Their effects usually become apparent between four and six months after the first application.

A Potent Formula

WHAT? Viagra

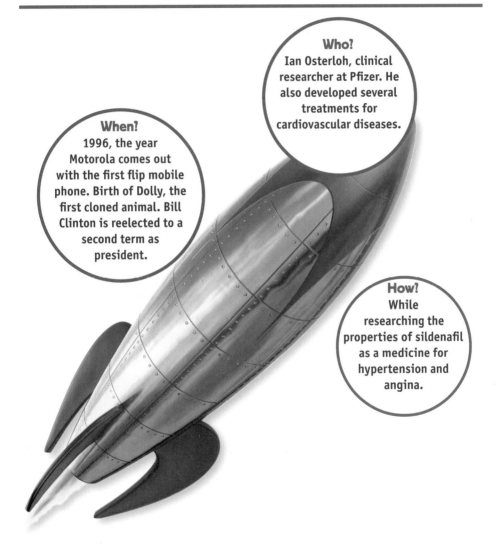

Who?
Ian Osterloh, clinical researcher at Pfizer. He also developed several treatments for cardiovascular diseases.

When?
1996, the year Motorola comes out with the first flip mobile phone. Birth of Dolly, the first cloned animal. Bill Clinton is reelected to a second term as president.

How?
While researching the properties of sildenafil as a medicine for hypertension and angina.

Viagra is undoubtedly one of the drugs that has caused the biggest stir in recent years. This miraculous blue pill generated (and continues to generate) great expectations among people suffering from sexual impotence. What few know is that this drug was discovered by chance. Here is the story of the discovery of the first effective oral treatment for erectile dysfunction.

In 1995, a group of pharmaceutical chemists at Pfizer led by Ian Osterloh were working with an active ingredient called sildenafil. Their aim was to produce a drug to combat high blood pressure and angina. But they changed course when Osterloh found that sildenafil induced notable erections in the patients tested. The reaction was so pronounced that Pfizer executives called for a change in strategy and developed sildenafil as the active ingredient in an oral treatment for impotence.

It was truly a blockbuster. In 1996, the drug was patented, and in 1998 the Food and Drug Administration (F.D.A.) approved the use of Viagra for treating erectile dysfunction. That same year it went on sale, supported by a million-dollar advertising campaign. Advertised on television, it was endorsed by celebrities such as Bob Dole and Pelé, the Brazilian soccer player. It was an instant commercial success. Currently, Viagra is available in two forms: an oral tablet (effective one hour after swallowing) and chewable Viagra (effective within 15 minutes).

Just keep in mind that Viagra is a prescription drug, and should only be taken after an accurate diagnosis.

Sildenafil, better known by its trade name Viagra, was first synthesized during research at Pfizer in England. In Sanskrit the word viaghra means "tiger." It was originally designed to combat high blood pressure and angina.

Where Did Life Come From?

WHAT? The Biggest Hydrothermal Vent

When?
2000, the year the final original *Peanuts* comic strip appears. First long-term crew on the International Space Station.

Who?
Donna Blackman, Deborah Kelley, Jeff Karson and other scientists, oceanographers, mineralogists, geologists and specialists in Earth science.

How?
During an underwater expedition to map the Mid-Atlantic Ridge near the Atlantis fracture zone.

. . . .

Suddenly, the camera captured something surprising: A spectral range of about 30 hydrothermal vents, chief among them being the largest white plume ever discovered.

. . . .

Hydrothermal vent on the ocean floor. Magma, very close to or on the surface of some parts of the ocean floor, emerges and causes vaporization of the nearest water, carrying along chemical elements that give it a blackish color. The rise in temperature of the environment enables life to exist.

This is not the place to delve deeply into the question of the origin of life on Earth. There are countless theories on the subject, some more accepted than others. It seems that what scientists do agree on is that life evolved from inert matter sometime between 4,400 and 2,700 million years ago.

One of the latest hypotheses was proposed in 2002 by Professor William Martin (University of Düsseldorf) and Dr. Michael Russell (Scottish Environmental Research Centre, University of Glasgow). Their theory argues that life on Earth originated from inorganic cells that emerged from the bottom of the oceans. According to them, life is a chemical consequence of hydrothermal fluid streams emerging from so-called hydrothermal vents in the Earth's crust, thousands of feet deep under the water. These are small caves whose walls are coated with a large quantity of metal sulfides. These are the elements that, according to Martin and Russell, reacted millions of years ago with the hydrothermal fluid, generating primordial cells.

The first known black vents (the dark color is due to iron content) were discovered in the late 1970s. These hydrothermal vents on the ocean floor reach temperatures of up to 750 degrees Fahrenheit. How do they form? Normally, the ocean floor increases at the rate of about 1.18 inches per year in the Mid-Ocean Ridge system. This causes cracks in the underwater crust from which emerges molten magma that originates in the Earth's mantle.

These underwater vents produce life around them, hosting communities (an abundance of worms, clams and shrimps) fed by the substances they emit.

The size of the vents discovered was about thirty-two feet high, that is, until serendipity led to the discovery of the so-called Lost City. The planet's largest fumarole (up to 197 feet high) was discovered by chance during a joint expedition of the American University of Washington, D.C. and Duke University, funded by the National Science Foundation. In December 2000, aboard the submersible *Alvin* (which also provided the first pictures of the wreckage of the sunken *Titanic*), a group of experts led by Donna Blackman, Deborah Kelley and Jeff Karson was mapping the Atlantis massif. It is an underwater dome-shaped region located about 8,200 feet deep in the Atlantic Ocean, halfway between Europe and America. Suddenly, the camera captured something surprising: a spectral range of about 30 hydrothermal vents, chief among them the largest white plume ever discovered.

Following this chance discovery, several expeditions have returned to the site. Research concludes that the hydrothermal vents of the Lost City (as it was named by its discoverers) release large amounts of methane and hydrogen and few metals (hence its characteristic white color). The soil of the zone consists of volcanic basalt, and groups of microorganisms and invertebrate species live in its environs. Scientists estimate that its activity dates back 30,000 years, and predict that it will remain active for thousands of centuries more.

Volcanic vents, when they are very close to each other, may come to resemble forests. Pressure prevents the water from boiling easily. Volcanic plumes or tuffs grow rapidly through the emission of copper, iron and zinc sulfides. Single-celled microorganisms called archaea grow in its environs, serving as food for larger species.

ARCHEOLOGY & HISTORY

Land Ho!

WHAT? The Discovery of America

When?
1492, Ferdinand and Isabella complete the Reconquista and expel the Jews from Spain.

Who?
Christopher Columbus (1451–1506), navigator and Mediterranean cartographer, a visionary.

How?
While looking for a route to Cipango (Japan) and the lands of the Great Khan in search of gold.

There is gold in abundance, but the monarch does not easily allow it to be removed from the island, so few merchants go there and rarely do ships from other regions arrive at their ports. The king of the island has a grand palace, roofed in very fine gold, in the way that those of our churches are coated with lead. Its windows are trimmed with gold, and the floors of the rooms and many of the chambers are covered with gold plates, of up to two fingers in thickness. Over there, pearls are extremely abundant, round, thick, and red, which makes them higher in price and more valuable than white ones. There are also many precious stones, so that the island of Cipango is wonderfully rich.

Marco Polo

The year was 1480, when the navigator and cartographer Christopher Columbus first read the reports of the Florentine mathematician and doctor Paolo dal Pozzo Toscanelli, who claimed it was possible to reach Cipango (now Japan) by sailing west. He had even drawn a map showing the exact route, inspired by the travels of Marco Polo. But the Venetian explorer had not been very well oriented during his travels: he stated that from the western tip of Europe (Lisbon) to Asia (Nanjing) was a short distance of 6,500 leagues.

But this was no simple mission. By the late thirteenth century, the brothers Ugolino and Vandino Vivaldi of Genoa had built two ships, and sailed through the Straits of Gibraltar, continuing southward along the coast of Africa. They were never heard from again. The Mare Tenebrosum (Atlantic Ocean) seemed unwilling to allow anyone to pass through, but one had to try. The Turks took Constantinople in 1453 and subsequently conquered Egypt. So finding a new route to the East Indies was ur-

Monument of Christopher Columbus on the Italian Riviera near Genoa, where, according to most sources, he was born. Despite this common belief, his birthplace is unknown, although it is known that he was educated in Italy and Portugal as a cartographer and a navigator.

gent. Portugal and Spain were big exporting powers and needed to find new navigation routes. Portuguese navigators cautiously began to explore the Atlantic coast of Africa, looking to skirt the southern tip and head for the Indies. It was an endeavor that inspired a young Christopher Columbus to appear at the court of the Portuguese king, Juan II, with an ambitious project: build three ships and load them with food and goods to trade in the East Indies, where he would declare himself admiral and governor of the discovered territories, and then be awarded ten percent of the profits. These conditions seemed excessive to the Lusitanian monarch, and he did not pay much attention to the proposal.

In 1485, Columbus was widowed and left Portugal for Spain. On January 20, 1486, he presented his project to the Spanish monarchs Ferdinand and Isabella. Since things proceeded slowly at the palace, it took the Spanish monarchs six years to respond to the navigator. Finally, in April, 1492, the famous Capitulations of Santa Fe (Granada) were signed, in which Christopher Columbus was appointed admiral, viceroy and governor general of all the territories that he would discover. He was also awarded ten percent of the profits to be made in the New World.

Prior to the sixteenth century, America did not appear on maps. Little by little it began to be drawn from east to west and it was not until the nineteenth century that the entire west coast of the United States had been explored. These two maps show how the cartography of Central America and North America evolved.

In the early hours of August 3, 1492, Christopher Columbus and eighty-seven men aboard three ships left the port of Palos de la Frontera on course to the Canary Islands. From there they continued westward, convinced that their masts were turned toward Cipango (Japan) and Cathay (China). At daybreak on October 12, 1492, purely by coincidence, they sighted what would be one of the greatest discoveries in history. The land they glimpsed was not the coveted East Indies, but a New World, America. Columbus first disembarked off the coast of San Salvador (Guanahani, Bahamas), convinced that he was

• •

Mistakenly, they referred to them as "Indians," convinced that they were inhabitants of the East Indies.

• •

walking on the first island of the Asian Indies. Here is how Fray Bartolome de las Casas recounted the historic arrival of Columbus in the New World:

At two hours past midnight, land came into view about two leagues away. All the sails were lowered save the cross-jack, which is the largest sail without bonnets, and they sailed close-hauled until Friday when they reached the small island of Lucayos, as it was called in the language of the Guanahani Indians.

Naked people came forth, and the Admiral went ashore in the armed ship with Martin Alonso Pinzon and Vicente Yanez, his brother, who was the captain of the Nina. The Admiral took the royal standard and the two captains carried two banners of the green cross, which the Admiral used for signaling in all of his ships, one with an F and one with a Y and a crown above each letter, one on one side of the cross, and the other on the other.

They went ashore and saw very green trees, a lot of water, and many different kinds of fruit. The Admiral called to the two captains and to the others, who leaped onshore, and to Rodrigo de Escobedo, clerk of the entire fleet, and to Rodrigo Sanchez de Segovia, and told them to bear faithful testimony that he, with all of us as witnesses, now took possession of that island in the name of the King and the Queen, his Lords making the requisite declarations, as is fully elaborated in the testimonies that were written there.

Toucans, one of the species of birds found in America, attracted great attention from the newly arrived travelers.

Later, many island people gathered there.

The island was inhabited by the Taino people, an indigenous race from what is now Venezuela. Mistakenly, they were referred to as "Indians," convinced that they were inhabitants of the East Indies. Columbus left a written account of his first impression of the natives:

> I knew that we might forge a great friendship, for I knew they were a people who could be more easily freed and converted to our holy faith by love than by force. Some of them were given red caps and glass beads to put around their necks, and many other things of little value, which gave them great pleasure, and made them so much our friends that it was a marvel to see. Afterwards they came to the ship's boats where we were swimming, and brought us parrots, cotton threads in skeins, darts and many other things; and we exchanged them for other things that we gave them, such as glass beads and small bells.

The first steps of Christopher Columbus onto the shores of the New World, in San Salvador on October 12, 1492, in a painting by Dióscoro Teófilo Puebla Tolín.

Which Way? East or West?

WHAT? The Discovery of Brazil

Who!
Pedro Álvares Cabral (1467–1520), aristocrat and Portuguese navigator in command of the second Portuguese fleet to India.

When!
1500, the year Pinzon discovers the Amazon for the Europeans and Pope Alexander VI inaugurates the University of Valencia.

How!
Departing from the African coast in order to avoid terrible storms in the area, after 43 days of travel, he sighted Mount Pascoal and, thinking that it was an island, named it the Island of Vera Cruz.

As had happened to Christopher Columbus eight years earlier, the nobleman and Portuguese navigator Pedro Álvares Cabral discovered Brazil by coincidence, convinced that he had arrived at another place.

Born in the Portuguese town of Belmonte, at the age of thirty-two he was appointed by King Manuel I of Portugal (1495–1521) to act as commander-in-chief of an extremely well equipped armada and ordered to sail to the East Indies, following the route of another illustrious Portuguese, Vasco da Gama. The great navigator, da Gama, had opened a new sea route from Europe to India, thus enabling trade with the Far East without having to use the costly and unsafe routes of the caravans traveling the so-called Silk Road.

The second Portuguese expedition to India was the best equipped of the fifteenth century. Comprising thirteen vessels (ten small boats and three ships) and a crew of 1,200, it sailed from the beach at Restelo (Lisbon) on March 9, 1500, with the mission of improving diplomatic and trade relations with India. The plan was to install a trading post there and to return laden with goods. For this expedition, they were to follow the route around the Cape of Good Hope, an achievable endeavor, since they could rely on some of the best sailors in the country, including Bartolomeu Dias, the first European explorer to reach the southern tip of Africa, Diogo Dias (brother of Bartolomeu), Pêro Vaz de Caminha, Sancho de Tovar and Nicolau Coelho.

Pedro Álvares Cabral studied literature, history and science, including cosmography and military arts, in Lisbon. He expanded his knowledge of cosmography and navigation at the court of Juan II, the "Perfect Prince," of Portugal. His successor, Manuel I, named Cabral captain of the armada that would leave for the Indies.

The expedition was to follow the route discovered by Vasco da Gama in 1497; but at a certain point, Pedro Álvares Cabral decided to change course in order to avoid fearsome storms in that area.

The idea was to follow the route discovered by Vasco da Gama in 1497; but at a certain point, Pedro Álvares Cabral decided to change course in order to avoid fearsome storms in that area. After passing the islands of Cape Verde, the expedition made an exaggerated westward turn, away from the African coast. By taking this route, the Portuguese armada encountered a wind current, the trade winds, which would eventually lead them to discover Brazil purely by serendipity. After forty-three days at sea, on April 22, 1500, and quite far from the coast, Cabral sighted Mount Pascoal on the southern coast of what is today the State of Bahia. The next day, he went ashore and, believing that it was an island, he named it the Island of Vera Cruz.

The Portuguese armada was convinced that these were the Indies (as had happened to Christopher Columbus) and remained on this coast until May 2. During that time, the crew made contact with the indigenous population, a description of which has survived to this day thanks to a letter by the secretary Pêro Vaz de Caminha, recounting the discovery and the first contacts of the Portuguese expedition of Pedro Álvares Cabral. Dated May 1, 1500, it was sent back to the court of King Manuel I on board a maintenance vessel. Here's an interesting passage:

> They are dark, half red, with good faces and well-formed noses. They go naked, without any type of covering. They are innocent about nudity, showing no more concern for covering themselves or their private parts than they do about showing their faces.
>
> Some walk around with pierced bottom lips, wherein is placed a genuine white bone, the length of a hand and as thick as a cotton spindle, the points sharp as if it were a bodkin. They put these bones in through the inner side of the lip and the part that remains in the mouth between the lips and teeth. It is shaped like a chess rook,

The discovery of Brazil and colonization by Europeans had a detrimental effect on the indigenous American population.

Parrots of the genus *Ara*, comprising 14 species living among the forests from Mexico to northeastern Argentina. These inhabitants of the southern hemisphere were among the amazing discoveries of early American explorers.

fitted in such a way that it does not hurt them nor prevent them from talking, eating or drinking.

They have straight hair. The top of their head is shaved, and the rest of the hair is shorn above the ears. One of them was wearing a type of headdress fashioned out of very large, long, yellow feathers that covered his neck and ears like en elongated lapel, draped from one side to the other. And it had been glued to the hair, feather by feather, with a white substance that looked like wax, so that the headdress was very round and full, very even, and did not need anything else to look complete.

After the accidental discovery of Brazil, the Portuguese expedition continued its route to Calicut (now Kozhikode, on the coast of the state of Kerala in southern India). During the voyage, they also discovered Madagascar. Cabral lost four of his ships when rounding the Cape of Good Hope, including, ironically, that of its discoverer, Bartolomeu Dias.

They finally returned to Lisbon on July 31, 1501, with only four out of the thirteen ships with which they had started.

A Fortunate Farmer

WHAT? The Venus de Milo

Who?
Yorgos Kentrotas, Greek farmer who was rummaging around the ruins in the ancient city of Milos, and Jules Dumont d'Urville, the French naval officer who appraised the find and sought help from the French ambassador to acquire it. In the struggle with the Greeks, the statue was dragged; this is supposedly how the arms were broken.

When?
1820, George IV becomes King of England; Florida is ceded to the United States, and Joseph Smith has a vision that will lead to the founding of The Church of Jesus Christ of Latter-day Saints.

How?
Half buried in two pieces on the Aegean island of Melos. Yorgos took one piece to his stable, since together they weighed about 1,900 pounds, and offered it to an Orthodox clergyman, who in turn offered it to a French mariner and explorer who recognized its value.

• •

Her name derives from the island of Milos (formerly Melos) on the
Cyclades archipelago in southeastern Greece, where she was
accidentally discovered on April 8, 1820.

• •

Venus de Milo (dated circa 100 B.C.E.) is one of the most
famous ancient sculptures, and has been exhibited in the
Louvre since 1821. It measures 6.7 feet in height, weighs
approximately 1,900 pounds and represents Aphrodite
(Venus in Roman mythology), the Greek goddess of love
and beauty. Sculpted in Parian marble, it consists of
carved segments (unusual at the time) and is a combination of different sculptural styles. The head of the goddess is typical of the late fifth century B.C.E.; her nudi-
ty, the fourth century B.C.E., and her posture with
multiple points-of-view is characteristic of the later Hel-
lenistic period. The sculptor is unknown, but other fragments were discovered next to her with inscriptions that
mention two artists from Antioch named Agesandros and
Aleixandros.

Her name derives from the island of Milos (formerly
Melos) on the Cyclades archipelago in southeastern
Greece, where she was accidentally discovered on April
8, 1820. That day, Yorgos Kentrotas, a farmer from Paleo
Castro (main town of the island), was quietly working the
land when his hoe met with the head of a large marble
statue that was split into two parts.

At that time, the French vessel Chevrette, captained
by Pierre Henri Gauttier Duparc, was sailing in Greek waters, conducting hydrographic surveys of the islands.
During a stopover in Milos, the local French representa-
tive brought the discovery of Venus to the attention of
the officer Jules Dumont d'Urville, who went to see it,

Milo is the name of the
small Greek volcanic island
where the Venus de Milo was
found. Milo was formed by
the remains of a volcano,
and many interesting
archaeological remains can be
found there.

immediately recognized the value of the work, and acquired it immediately. The sculpture was given to King Louis XVIII and finally moved to the Louvre Museum where it remains to this day.

There are several theories about the original position of her lost arms. The most accepted is that in one hand she was holding an apple (according to the myth) and with the other, gathering up the robe that seems to fall from her waist.

Below: The Louvre Museum, where the Venus de Milo is kept.

The Apple of Discord

Zeus organized a sumptuous banquet to celebrate the wedding of Peleus and Thetis but did not invite Eris, goddess of discord. She went to the party anyway and dropped a golden apple that bore the inscription: "To the most beautiful."

Three goddesses immediately claimed the apple: Hera, Athena and Aphrodite. Zeus appointed Paris of Troy to judge between them. Each goddess used her wiles to convince Paris. Hera promised him power over men, Athena offered wisdom, and Aphrodite promised him the love of Helen, the most beautiful woman in the world.

Paris did not hesitate for a second, choosing Aphrodite's offering. As a consequence, Helen abandoned her husband Menelaus, thus precipitating the Trojan War.

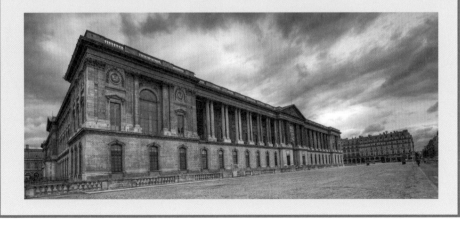

A Lucky Soldier

WHAT? The Rosetta Stone

When?
1799, the year of Napoleon's November coup. In July, during his campaign in Egypt, the Rosetta Stone is discovered. In Germany, Carl Friedrich Gauss establishes the Fundamental Theorem of Algebra.

Who?
Pierre-François Bouchard (1772–1832), French army captain who accompanied Napoleon's campaign in Egypt. While there, he passed his final examination from the École Polytechnique. He attained the rank of battalion chief.

How?
When carrying out the fortification of Fort Saint-Julien, a mere 2.5 miles from the town of Rosetta, with the discovery of a stone of black basalt.

Archeological discoveries have always been closely linked to all kinds of serendipities. You never know what you are going to find in an excavation, although obviously you know that there is something and you are looking for it.

Archeologists have a very special relationship with luck. This does not mean that they place all of their work, experience and wisdom in the hands of the Goddess of Fortune, but they do often end up finding something different or simply not what they had been looking for. The history of archeology has given us many intriguing stories. One of the more remarkable, given the importance of the find, occurred during the Napoleonic wars in the eighteenth century.

The Rosetta Stone was discovered by the French during Napoleon's campaign in Egypt. It was confiscated by the British before it could brought to France, and ended up in the British Museum in London, where it has remained since 1802.

In the summer of 1799, Napoleon and his troops were in Egypt, waging a campaign against the British. The French had underestimated the enemy's strength and had begun to consider withdrawing.

The Gallic troops were on the northern coast of the country on July 15, when they began to dig a defensive ditch near a port town called Rosetta. Leading the troops was Captain Pierre-François Bouchard, in charge of the operation to fortify Fort Saint-Julien. While digging, a soldier's shovel struck a hard surface: a large black granite slab. When they removed it, they saw that it was covered in strange inscriptions, and the captain immediately reported the discovery to Napoleon. There were several scholars of Egyptian culture among the men who accompanied Bonaparte on this campaign, and the task of making the first interpretation of this strange discovery was assigned to them.

Thomas Young (1773–1829) of the Royal Society of London, was one of the first to attempt to decipher the Rosetta Stone. He had made notable discoveries in such fields as light, energy, physiology and language. Young translated the demotic text on the stone, but when it came to the hieroglyphics, it was the French linguist Jean-François Champollion who published the famous translation.

The scholars quickly realized that the stone contained three different scripts. The first was hieroglyphic, and the third was Greek. The intermediate inscription later proved to be demotic, a late form of Egyptian writing. The French took the stone to Cairo, where Bonaparte had founded a school for the study of ancient Egyptian civilization. Copies of the stone were made and sent to France for examination, while the original stone was left in the custody of General de Menou at his private residence in Alexandria. There it remained until 1801, when the French capitulated to British troops, who confiscated all of the Egyptian antiquities collected by the expedition, including the Rosetta Stone.

One of the first scholars to address the interpretation of the black granite stele was the English scientist Thomas Young, who published his findings in a famous article in the *Encyclopaedia Britannica*. He would later claim that his writings should be cited as the basis for another translation by the linguist Jean-François Champollion, considered by many as the father of Egyptology.

The text engraved on the stone was the Memphis Decree of March 27, 196 B.C.E., made during the reign of Ptolemy V. It describes various taxes that the king had revoked and contains a complex formula for making gratuities to the sovereign:

· ·

While digging, a soldier's shovel struck a hard surface: a large black granite slab.

· ·

In the reign of the youth who has succeeded his father in sovereignty, Lord of the royal insignia, most glorious, the establisher of order in Egypt, pious towards the gods, triumphant over his enemies, who has restored the life of men, Lord of the Thirty Years' Festival, equal to Hefaistos the Great, a king like the Sun, Great King of the Upper and Lower countries, descendant of the gods Philopator, to whom Hephaestus has bestowed approbation, to whom the Sun has given victory, the living image of Zeus, son of the Sun, Ptolemy, living forever, beloved of Ptah, in the ninth year, when Aetos, son of Aetos, was priest of Alexander, and the gods Soteres, and the gods Adelphi, and the gods Euergetes Eucharistos; Pyrrha, daughter of Philinos, being Athlophoros of Berenike Euergetis; Aria, daughter of Diogenes, being Kanephoros of Arsinoe Philadelphos; Irene, daughter of Ptolemy, being priestess of Arsinoe Philopator, the fourth day of the month of Xandikos.

Jean-François Champollion (1831), by Leon Cogniet. Champollion, has gone down in history for his translation of the Rosetta Stone. By the age of sixteen, he had already mastered a dozen languages.

Today the Rosetta Stone is on exhibit at the British Museum in London. It has only been removed once. In 1972, it was temporarily exhibited at the Louvre Museum to commemorate the 150th anniversary of the deciphering of the hieroglyphics.

There's Gold in Them Thar Hills

WHAT? The California Gold Rush

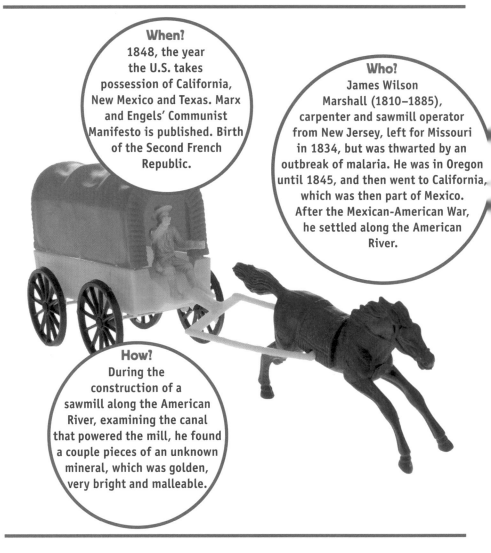

When?
1848, the year the U.S. takes possession of California, New Mexico and Texas. Marx and Engels' Communist Manifesto is published. Birth of the Second French Republic.

Who?
James Wilson Marshall (1810–1885), carpenter and sawmill operator from New Jersey, left for Missouri in 1834, but was thwarted by an outbreak of malaria. He was in Oregon until 1845, and then went to California, which was then part of Mexico. After the Mexican-American War, he settled along the American River.

How?
During the construction of a sawmill along the American River, examining the canal that powered the mill, he found a couple pieces of an unknown mineral, which was golden, very bright and malleable.

It all began in 1839 when settler John A. Sutter took possession of 76 square miles of land in Coloma, California, in the valley of the American River. He named it New Helvetia (Sutter was of Swiss descent) and created a prosperous agricultural settlement, extensively planted with fruit orchards and cereals, and with a herd of livestock, comprising thousands of cattle, sheep and horses.

One day while watching the flow of the river that crossed his land, it occurred to him that he could utilize it for hydraulic energy to power a sawmill. So he contacted a local carpenter, James Wilson Marshall, to oversee the project.

As chance would have it, on January 24, 1848, Marshall discovered some yellow particles that flashed in the sunlight in the riverbed. He took the stones, wrapped them in a handkerchief and ran to show Sutter his chance discovery. There was no doubt about it: these were real nuggets of pure gold. But the public was yet to know what had just been found. It was a discovery that would unleash the largest collective madness in modern history: the California Gold Rush.

Given the importance of the discovery, Sutter wanted to keep it a secret, fearing that the curious, or even worse, fortune seekers would arrive on his property in droves. So it was business as usual in New Helvetia until Sutter made a mistake: he wanted to claim the titles for the valley of Coloma and for some land beyond his property. He delegated the task to his employee Charles Bennet, who went to San Francisco to get the land titles from the governor. The man was not entirely discrete, and the news spread through the city like wildfire. On March 15 of that same year, the newspaper *The Californian* published the news, and in August, the *New York Herald* announced the discovery to the east coast of the country. On December 5, 1848, in an address to the U.S. Congress, the nation's president,

Prospector or gold digger with all of his equipment. They still exist today in some parts of the world, such as northern Finland.

A single ounce of gold weighs 31.10 grams, and can be molded so that it covers 33 square yards. The main attractions of gold are its malleability and color.

• •

Marshall did not even know what gold looked like, but Sutter quickly identified these golden and easily malleable nuggets as the most desired metal in the world.

• •

Port of San Francisco in 1830–1831. A mecca for gold prospectors, in Spanish times it was called Yerba Buena. It was renamed when it became a U.S. city in 1846. The Gold Rush caused the population to increase from 1,000 inhabitants in 1848 to 25,000 a year later. Sailors abandoned their ships in the harbor and took off for the mountains. Levi Strauss settled there right away and began producing his pants with pockets riveted to withstand the hard labor of the prospectors.

James Polk, officially announced what had been discovered in the American River. A great influx of immigrants started coming to California, dreaming of gold. The population of San Francisco soared. Given the lack of buildings, the new arrivals stayed wherever they could: in tents, cabins, sheds and boats. Known as the "forty-niners" (the year of their arrival), they were everywhere.

Settlements appeared and disappeared depending on where gold nuggets were found. In 1849, about 90,000 people came to California in search of gold. By 1855, gold prospectors and traders attracted by the business amounted to more than 300,000 people from all over the world, including China, France, the Philippines, Spain and even Africa. Gold prospectors earned quite a good living from their findings, and the traders even more so. One of the most fortunate was Samuel Brannan, owner of a chain of shops that provided everything the forty-niners needed.

Interestingly, John A. Sutter, owner of the land where the first gold nuggets were discovered, did not become rich because of this discovery. On the contrary, his lands were literally invaded by prospectors, and all of his workers left their posts to try their luck at easy gold.

Find of the Century (I)

WHAT? The Dead Sea Scrolls

Who?
Mohammed ed-Dhib and his cousin Jum'a, Bedouin shepherds from the Ta'amireh tribe. They offered the scrolls to a dealer in Bethlehem who did not want them, to a Syrian Christian merchant, and then to an antiques dealer; from there they went to a monastery, later to an Orthodox archbishop and finally to two archeologists from the University of Jerusalem.

When?
1947, the year the IMF begins operations. First supersonic flight. *The Plague* by Albert Camus is published.

How?
By throwing a stone into one of many crevices in an area where they were shepherding. They could tell from the sound that the interior space was fairly large. They went in and brought out a pot that contained several scrolls. One of these was the *Isaiah Scroll*.

· ·

The goat hopped into a hole and refused to leave. The shepherd threw a stone inside and found that it was very deep.

· ·

The Dead Sea Scrolls are a priceless collection of almost eight hundred texts written in Hebrew and Aramaic, possibly compiled by the Essenes, a Jewish sect. All of the scrolls were found in eleven caves near the Dead Sea. The search began in 1947 after the chance discovery of seven scrolls. This discovery could not have been more coincidental.

There have been nomads in the region of the West Bank since biblical times. Even today, it is not uncommon to find shepherds with their flocks of goats camped at the gates of Jerusalem, especially on the eastern side, which is desert and descends to the Dead Sea. The Qumran manuscripts were found in this region.

Mohammed ed-Dhib, a Bedouin shepherd from the Ta'amireh tribe, was looking for a lost goat in a cave at Qumran, on the shores of the Dead Sea. With the intention of chasing it out, he threw a stone into the dark interior and squarely hit a full jar of clay. The sound seemed unusual. Filled with curiosity, he entered the cave to see where the sound came from. Inside, he found several jars with wooden lids containing written scrolls that were carefully wrapped in linen. The most widely accepted theory is that the owners had hidden them to protect them as the Roman soldiers advanced into the area around 70 B.C.E. Most of the discovered texts date from 250 B.C.E. to 66 B.C.E.

But what are the contents of these scrolls? Among the manuscripts are:

- The books of the Tanakh (the Hebrew Scriptures), including a longer version of 1 Samuel
- Manuals, regulations and prayers unique to the community that inhabited the site, among which the Damascus Document stands out
- The Testaments of the Twelve Patriarchs
- The Book of Jubilees

- A copper roll relating the locations of certain treasures.

The texts are key to a clearer understanding of how Christianity and Judaism developed, since many emphasize fundamental issues highlighted by Jesus and the Christians in their writings, such as the coming of the Son of God, the Holy Spirit, baptism, the sacrament of bread and wine, the Fall of the Kings and the resurrection. Thus they are a clear and immediate antecedent to what the Gospels contain.

Here is a short excerpt from one of the texts found in the caves of the Dead Sea:

For heaven and earth will hear the Messiah, and none will depart from the holy precepts. Seekers of God, strengthen yourselves in His service! All with hope in their heart, in this will you not find the Lord? For the Lord will watch over the pious and call the righteous, the Holy Spirit will hover over the poor, and renew the faithful with His power. As He will honor the pious upon the throne of His eternal kingdom, liberating prisoners, giving sight to the blind, and straightening out the dishonest. He will join forever with those who wait. In His mercy, He will judge, and no one will be denied the fruit of the good work. And the Lord will accomplish glorious things which have never existed before, as He has said, and then the wounded will be healed, the dead will be resurrected, good tidings will be given to the poor, the homeless will be sheltered, castaways will be guided and the hungry will be enriched.

Region of the Qumran caves at the Dead Sea. The Israelis have installed a modern museum, where some of the manuscripts are exhibited, next to the excavations at Qumran, on the road from the Gulf of Aqaba to Jerusalem, where you can also eat, buy souvenirs, and visit the ruins.

The Find of the Century (II)

WHAT? The Qin Terracotta Army

When?
1974, the year the Mariner spacecraft flies over Mercury for the first time. Isabel Peron, first female president in the world, takes office in Argentina.

Who?
A group of Chinese farmers, who in a very dry year decided to dig a well. On the third day, one of them, by the name of Yang Zhifa, found a ceramic head that he mistook for a jar. The first to recognize the importance of the discovery was Zhao Kangmin, head of cultural relics at the Lintong Museum.

How?
While digging a well about a mile from Mount Li, in the suburbs of Xi'an, Shaanxi Province.

- -

The emperor of China, Qin Shi Huang believed that in the afterlife those thousands of soldiers would continue to be at his service.

- -

One of the most spectacular archeological deposits in history (comparable to the tomb of Tutankhamun) was found by chance while a group of farmers was digging a well in search of water.

It happened in 1974 about eighteen miles from Xi'an, in Shaanxi Province in the People's Republic of China. Several remains had already been unearthed in that area, but the local people did not attach much importance to these findings, and even reburied them because it was thought that they brought bad luck. This attitude changed when, while digging a well, they came across a large pit containing over 7,000 life-size terracotta figures of soldiers, with distinct traits and grouped in the order of battle: archers, crossbowmen, infantry, cavalry and chariots.

A similar army had been buried, circa 210 B.C.E., to guard the mausoleum of the self-proclaimed first emperor of China, Qin Shi Huang. This emperor, obsessed with immortality, is credited with great works, including the construction of the Great Wall. However, this was always at the expense of the labor of slaves who fueled his delusions. It is estimated that the construction of the Terracotta Army lasted for about forty years and that more than 700,000 workers took part. What is most striking is that because they were molded one by one, all of the figures have distinct features: mustaches, hairstyles, and of various ages and ethnic groups — an absolute variety.

The heads and bodies of the terracotta warriors are hollow. There are more than 6,000 bodies of an average height of five feet, nine inches. Each one is unique. Every soldier originally carried an armament, but these were looted after the fall of the Qin dynasty. Due to oxidation, the vivid colors of the figures were lost within five hours of unearthing them, and therefore all appear gray.

The heads and hands were molded separately and then later added to the bodies.

In 1976, a second pit was found, located sixty-five feet away from the first. Smaller, it houses a collection of cavalry comprising over 1,400 pieces, including horses and riders divided into fourteen rows and protected by archers. Soon thereafter, a third pit was found, the smallest of all, with sixty-eight figures of officials, commanders and generals. The three pits are between thirteen and twenty-six feet deep, and the excavation site has come to be called the Qinshihuang Mausoleum Museum. An empty fourth pit indicated to archeologists that the emperor's plan had originally been even more lavish, but his death ended the work.

The great artificial hill where the body of the emperor is believed to be buried remains unexcavated, although work is ongoing, and interesting findings continue to emerge. Figures of beardless warriors, sculptures of young recruits (perhaps seventeen years old) and 114 figures that still retain their vivid color pigmentation were recently discovered.

Of the three pits, the second is open to the public, and is known as the pit of generals, for they likely represent the highest command. It also contains four horses.

Other Serendipities

How?
For serendipity to occur you have to be prepared, although, sometimes, you can cheat a little. For example, if you are a biologist and visit the basement of an old museum of natural history, where discoveries made long ago are accumulated without having been classified, you might find a new species of lizard.

Interestingly, phosphorus is found in semen. This makes it possible to detect with ultraviolet rays and has enabled some criminal cases to be solved.

Iodine is very corrosive in pure form, but when combined with povidone, it is an excellent disinfectant.

Phosphorous
1669

Hennig Brandt (1630–1710) was a German merchant and amateur alchemist in search of the so-called Philosopher's Stone. To find this substance, supposedly capable of turning base metals into gold, he experimented by heating and mixing human urine with all kinds of substances. After heating one of these mixtures, he obtained a solid residue that emitted a curious pale green glow. He had just discovered phosphorus. Its name means "light-bearer," because its original form, not found in nature, combines with oxygen and oxidizes, spontaneously emitting light.

Pallas
1802

The second asteroid discovered in the asteroid belt, and the third largest in size, was discovered accidentally by the German physician and astronomer Heinrich Olbers (1758–1840). It happened while he was making observations in order to locate and determine the orbit of Ceres, the smallest dwarf planet in our solar system. Olbers named it in honor of Pallas Athena, the Greek goddess of wisdom.

Iodine
1811

Bernard Courtois (1777–1838) was a French manufacturer of potassium nitrate, who was looking for an alternative to wood ashes for obtaining this compound. Among other raw materials, he had begun to experiment with seaweed, which was very abundant on the coasts of Normandy and Brittany. One day in 1811, while attempting to isolate the compounds of sodium and potassium from the ashes of seaweed, he accidentally discovered a new chemical element. When using sulfuric acid to clean a substance that had reacted with a copper container, he observed the formation of a purple vapor. He had just discovered iodine.

Insulin
1889

Doctors Joseph von Mering (1849–1908) and Oskar Minkowski (1858–1931) were researching the function of the pancreas. To determine whether it was necessary for life, they removed one from the body of a dog. After the operation, an assistant happened to observe that the dog's urine had attracted a swarm of flies. When they analyzed it, they found that it was loaded with glucose, a common sign of diabetes. In this way, von Mering and Minkowski discovered for the first time the relationship between the pancreas and this disease. They continued their research until they proved that the pancreas produces a secretion that regulates sugar: insulin.

The relationship between the pancreas and diabetes was discovered through an experiment on dogs. Dogs and cats can suffer from this disease, which is detected by a greater than normal need to drink and urinate.

Anaphylaxis
1902

Charles Richet (1850–1935) was a French physician who was commissioned to investigate the toxic properties of the Portuguese man o' war, *Physalia physalis*. When under threat, this animal uses its tentacles to inject powerful venom. In order to find a protective serum, he began to experiment with the substance. Having no *Physalia,* he chose to use *Anemona sulcata*, which can be obtained in large quantities on the rocky shores of the Mediterranean. A dog named Neptune was the first subject of his experiments. Inoculated with a small dose of poison, the animal manifested typical symptoms: hives, somnolence and a drop in temperature. A month later, he injected it again with the same dose, and the dog died after half an hour. It had just suffered anaphylaxis, a generalized immune reaction of the body to contact with an allergen with which one has previously had contact.

Bakelite
1907
Leo Baekeland (1863–1944) came up with this cheap and versatile plastic while trying to solve a problem of chemical synthesis based on phenol and formaldehyde. Bakelite was the first in a series of synthetic resins that would revolutionize the modern economy and start the so-called Age of Plastic. Plastic has some interesting qualities. It is very hard due to the crosslinking of molecules. It is heat stable, so it can be molded as it is formed, and once it cools it cannot be melted again and reshaped. This is why it is used for the handles of pans.

Lascaux Cave
1940
Four teenagers, Marcel Ravidat, Jacques Marsal, Georges Agnel and Simon Coencas, were playing around a cave near Montignac in France. In the forest, there was a deep depression in the ground created many years ago by the fall of a great tree. The youths crawled inside and came to a larger space, now known as the Great Hall of Bulls. It was there on September 12, 1940, that they encountered an impressive sanctuary of Paleolithic paintings. The cave was opened to the public after the Second World War, but the carbon dioxide emitted by more than a thousand visitors daily damaged the paintings to the point that it was closed in 1963, and reproductions of the paint-

Physalia physalis, also known as the Portuguese man o' war, is a large jellyfish with a very painful sting. It only lives in warm waters, but global warming is enabling it to reach the northernmost coasts. Actually, it is not a jellyfish, but a colony of specialized minute individuals that divide the work. The pneumatophore makes it float and sail, gastrozooids enable digestion, dactylozooids create poison for hunting and defense, and gonozooids serve for reproduction.

ings were displayed within walking distance. The same year that it was discovered, this wonderful example of Paleolithic art was declared a historical monument.

Velcro
1941

George de Mestral (1907–1990) was a Swiss engineer who enjoyed walking with his dog in the countryside. One morning in 1941, upon returning from one of his excursions, he noticed that his pet's fur was full of thistles, as were his trousers. As he tried to detach them, he was surprised by the tenacity of these seeds and decided to examine them under a microscope. He saw that they were covered with a multitude of tiny hooks that acted as strong claws that cling to animal fur and fabric. This gave him the idea to create a revolutionary closure system that would be secure, and by virtue of its simplicity would be superior to any other previous system. In 1951, de Mestral patented his invention, Velcro, a word that comes

Replica of the cave paintings of Lascaux near Montignac, 650 feet away from the original cave. The replicas, which are facsimiles of the paintings and the original rock structures, protect the original paintings from carbon dioxide produced by visitors. The Cave of Altamira in Spain was also discovered by chance in 1879, when María, the eight-year-old daughter of Marcelino Sanz de Sautuola, slipped into a crevice while she was following her dog. She told her father, "Look, Dad, painted oxen!" Marcelino, who was fond of prehistory, publicized the discovery.

from the combination of the initial syllables of the French words velours ("velvet") and crochet ("hook").

Superglue
1942

The most powerful glue on the market is nothing but a substance called cyanoacrylate, accidentally invented by Dr. Harry Coover. In the Second World War, he sought a new substance for making highly transparent synthetic rangefinders for use in rifles. This is how he discovered superglue, which he ended up dismissing as being too sticky. Years later, the Eastman Kodak company redis-covered the substance and began to give it its current application. It is such a powerful adhesive that it is even used instead of surgical sutures in minor surgery to hold together human tissue. It was first used during the Viet-nam War to hold together wounds, including internal tis-sues, pending conventional surgery. No pressure or heat is required to adhere objects together; it is activated by contact with small amounts of water.

Harry Coover was working for the Eastman Kodak company when he discovered superglue. In 1942, his team was investigating a highly transparent plastic for rifle scopes. He rejected cyanoacrylate because it was too sticky. Nine years later, while trying to find a heat-resistant polymer for aircraft cabins, they tried it out again, and Coover realized what he had discovered.

Temple of Mithras
1954

The air raids that London suffered during the Second World War left much of the city in ruins. For the Roman and Mediaeval London Excavation Coun-cil, this was an opportunity to be-gin look-

ing for traces of Londinium, founded by the Romans around 43 C.E. In the midst of this endeavor, on Walbrook Street, they came upon a temple dedicated to Mithras, a cultic figure worshipped by the legionnaires. It had been constructed in the third century C.E. Among the ruins were other deities as well, such as Serapis, who was one of the favorites of the Roman soldiers.

Charon
1978

On June 22, 1978, James W. Christy (1938–), an astronomer at the United States Naval Observatory, noticed something peculiar when he was observing images of Pluto. The shape of the planet appeared slightly elongated, while stars appearing on the same photographs showed no such distortion. This indicated that there was another object orbiting periodically around the planet. Christy had just discovered the first moon of Pluto (now five are known). It measures about 753 miles in diameter, slightly more than half of Pluto, and was given the name Charon, after the mythical ferryman responsible for conducting the souls of the dead across the river Styx to Hades.

Statue of Mithras in the Circus Maximus in Rome. A temple, built in the third century C.E. and dedicated to this divinity, was discovered on Walbrook Street in London

To Find Out More

Finding evidence for a particular topic can also be coincidental. Serendipity is caused by a fortuitous accumulation of random facts that provoke us unconsciously. And that's just what happens when we go into a bookstore or library looking for information on something specific. There we are, with some idea of what we want and open to meeting our objective. Without knowing it, we have just entered the world of serendipities. We trail along between the aisles and shelves with a singular purpose and predisposed mind that will help us to find what we seek, often purely by chance.

This open and enterprising spirit is the main breeding ground for coincidences. And something like this happened to most of the protagonists in this book: doctors, researchers, archeologists, navigators, shrewd people ready to let their inquiries lead them to make big discoveries through a chance event. Picasso said that inspiration comes from working, and we could add: when you least expect it.

The Internet is another universe that is rife with serendipities. We enter it looking, say, for a specific date and that starts us out upon an infinite chain linking to further information. Online search engines are an open door to serendipity. We could say that the possibilities are endless. Hence, it is important to know how to separate the wheat from the chaff. This is tedious work, but we have put it together for you in this list of recommendations:

PETER J. BOWLER and IWAN RHYS MORUS, *Making Modern Science: A Historical Survey* 2005, University of Chicago Press.

DONALD CARDWELL, *The Norton History of Technology*, 1995, W.W. Norton.

LESLIE ALAN HORVITZ, *Eureka! Scientific Breakthroughs that Changed the World*, 2002, Wiley.

STEPHEN F. MASON, *A History of the Sciences*, 1962, Macmillan.

PAUL MURDIN, *Secrets of the Universe: How We Discovered the Cosmos*, 2009, University of Chicago Press.

R. PÉREZ TAMAYO, *Ciencia, paciencia y conciencia*, 1991, Siglo XXI Editores, México.

R. PÉREZ TAMAYO, *Serendipia. Ensayos sobre ciencia, medicina y otros sueños*, 2000, Siglo XXI Editores, México.

ROYSTON M. ROBERTS, *Serendipity: Accidental Discoveries in Science*, 1989, Wiley.

PERE ROMANILLOS, *Great Historical Blunders: Mistakes That Changed the Course of Science, Technology and History*, 2016, Konecky & Konecky.

SIMON SINGH, *Big Bang: The Origin of the Universe*, 2005, Harper Perennial.

RICHARD WESTFALL, *Never at Rest: A Biography of Isaac Newton*, 1983, Cambridge University Press.

JOHN WILLIAM HILL and DORIS K. KOLB, *Chemistry for Changing Times* (9th Edition), 2000, Prentice Hall.

Picture credits

a = above; **b** = below

DREAMSTIME

WIKIPEDIA COMMONS
84b BY Mattia Luigi Nappi; **97a** BY Jotquadrat; **105** BY Klewic; **162b** BY GrahamColm at en.wikipedia; **165** BY Ed Uthman; **167** BY Afriend of Akshay Sharma; **195** BY Hans Hillewaert